Making the Product Development FrameWORK

Insights from the Frontlines

C.R. Galluzzo
Deanna Bolton

Intel
PRESS

ISBN 13 978-1-934053-34-8

Publisher: Richard Bowles
Editor: David J. Clark
Program Manager: Stuart Douglas
Text Design & Composition: STI
Graphic Art:, Ted Cyrek, Ron Bohart (cover)

Library of Congress Cataloging in Publication Data:

Printed in the USA

10 9 8 7 6 5 4 3 2 1

First printing, September 2011

IMPORTANT

You can access the companion Web site for this book on the Internet at:

www.intel.com/intelpress/plc

Use the serial number located in the upper-right hand corner of the last page to register your book and access additional material, including the Digital Edition of the book.

Contents

Foreword

This book is a case study demonstrating everything change agents know about continuous and transformative organizational change. It is not about specifying and diagramming the steps of a product life cycle. "Product Life Cycle" (PLC) is a metaphor for a process that is nearly miraculous: how things as inert as silicon become as tiny and vital as a brain cell. A product only takes on life because humans agree to make it together and for each other. Then they align their behavior with that agreement—they change and revitalize their organizations.

The authors show us where to start: anywhere. The human organization is a system—it is "equifinal"—meaning you can touch it anywhere and it notices you everywhere.

The authors started at what was then the periphery of the organization— the design and manufacture of motherboards and systems. They didn't find the right place to touch until they found a sore spot—a place where the system was in pain: bad products provoking a key customer. There were confused output expectations, nonexistent performance feedback systems, and broken communications between those accountable for corrective action. The authors—key change agents—entered the system through this small, open sore. Turning away from their theories of product life cycle and dealing with the basics of human performance, they began swimming upstream in the flow of new products—up the chain of prerequisite subsystems—each with its own pain and its own form of resistance to having the sore treated.

The first practical version of the PLC came into existence—a framework for talking about output requirements in regular work-review management meetings. It generated guidelines, templates, and training tools—making it easy for people to get over their delusions of self-sufficiency, denial of failure, and fear of punishment. It made it easy and safe for people to learn—the key behavior in organizational change.

The usefulness of the PLC in treating the breakdown between design engineering and manufacturing caught the attention of another very different organization—a cross-functional group responsible for the New Product Introduction Process. This new ally refined the PLC for application to life-and-death decisions about new product ideas. The network of early adopters was expanded.

By 1998, a multimillion-dollar recall of the organization desktop motherboard became a catalyst to further improve the product development process. The "Joint Intel PLC Forum," which for the first time included the software community, became the arena in which these two mutually disrespectful professions had to tear down their walls and do a major remodeling of the PLC.

A series of successes opened doors to full acceptance of the PLC by the Corporate Quality Network. It facilitated a strong new emphasis on defect prevention in the company's core quality programs. In seven years, moving upstream from sores to critical wounds, always attending to the unique and critical details of each crisis, the PLC became the framework for most of the company's product development organizations.

In 2003, three different product development groups began to independently deal with the problem of platform coordination. Again, customer pain drove efforts further upstream to predict end-user needs and usage models. The disparate groups found the PLC a helpful framework on which to hang their uniquely complex requirements for coordination.

Early usefulness to the emergence of platform competence put the PLC front and center in Intel's next major transformation—what Paul Otellini called "a right-hand turn to Intel 3.0." Intel foresaw its evolution following a path from memory to microprocessors to becoming a "platform company." In 2004 the Corporate Platform Office was established, and a massive effort at articulating its strategy began. For more than a year, task forces in every part of the corporation were engaged in defining a Platform Program Life Cycle (PPLC.) Over the next few years, the PPLC had been put to hard use, stripped of much of its bulk, and pointed toward a whole new set of issues.

Today the complexity of the issues in the new environment is beyond comprehension. It can only be accomplished by many parallel acts of massive destruction and re-creation. The Product Life Cycle Framework has turned out to be a primary tool for harnessing that explosion of creativity and change. It became a corporate-wide framework allowing people in all the organization's subsystems—and much of the global society within which it operates—to make and honor their commitments to each other.

This remarkable tale is told with the quiet humility of a confession. The authors let us hear a few of the story's heroes. Even from the heroes we hear about doubts and long bouts of wrestling—not many moments of declarative leadership. And the authors, who rolled this stone up the hill every day, are especially quick to admit to errors. They ask really good questions as often as they draw conclusions. When they tell their truths, they credit others. They speak with the maturity and restraint of people who are a part of something greater than themselves—a very ambitious, intelligent, and important community of interdependent humans.

More reliable products and increased revenues are only partial measures of the value of the Product Life Cycle Framework. Perhaps of even greater value, it is a tool for peace-making. It provides a series of level playing fields and ground rules by which ambition, competency, and integrity are assessed. It nudges the organization further toward transparent meritocracy. It prevents the human relationships from disintegrating under the increasing pressures of complexity and uncertainty. It keeps the organization's outputs, and the organization itself, alive.

This book should be read quickly, then slowly. Pay attention to the questions. Then turn to the nearest painful symptom of miscommunication and kiss your silo goodbye.

William R. Daniels
American Consulting and Training, Inc.
Mill Valley, California

Preface

Anyone that develops products has some kind of a life cycle in their head when they come to work. People who develop products naturally think about market and technology forces coming together to form an opportunity for a product so consistent with strategy and roadmap that they have to plan it out. The product is then developed, verified, validated, released, ramped into manufacturing, sold, and eventually retired. Everyone who develops a product has their own unique picture of a life cycle in their head; the problem comes when you get a bunch of people together to develop a product, each with a different life cycle vision.

These differences can span anything from sequencing of big events, different names for the same event or, worse, the same event name meaning different things. The larger the development organization, the more globally dispersed, the more collaboration needed between distinct organizations, then the greater the need for a common product life cycle (PLC) definition.

A PLC is not really a process. Rather, it is an agreed-upon framework, a coat rack if you will, upon which you can hang process and tools that enable you to develop products in line with your business objectives. This framework should never be a statement of product development utopia, but rather a reflection of the maturity of your product development capability at any given point in time. It contains elements proven to contribute to business results along with those elements you aspire to change in order to improve business results in a reasonable amount of time.

Since the PLC is constantly maturing, it is never done and therefore conformance is not the ultimate measure of success. Success is not wasting resources relearning things already learned and consistently improving product development from a known baseline. Implementing suggests that once you do it you are done. In this book, implementing a life cycle means not only applying a framework to affect product development, but also the infrastructure for learning and continuing maturity going forward.

This book is not the official product development book of Intel dealing with the complexities of such things as circuit design, software development and technology transfer which Intel has successfully executed for many years. This book is about implementing a PLC to make those things better where the Intel experience is the basis of the story, but not the point. This story is about how a PLC can be implemented and evolved told anecdotally by the people on the front lines who actually develop products. The quotes inserted in the text are important, not add-ons; they are the story, the *insights from the people on the frontlines*. This is about how product development organizations can apply the PLC framework and make it *work* to improve business results. In that regard their story is about change agency as much or more than about the PLC.

The PLC now spans much of the company, but it of course did not start that way. Each chapter of the book is like a three-act play. The PLC has come a long way from its humble beginnings, and there were hard lessons learned along the way. First comes the opening disconfirming event, followed by the story of how the obstacles were removed, and ending with resolution and reflection. The questions at the end of the chapters are about subjects readers should consider to make this material more relevant to them and their organization.

Whereas the PLC flows from left to right moving from ideation through exploration and planning and into development before being released to production, this book, this story, is told from right to left. This is an example of how an organization can mature. The idea is that downstream recipients know full well the effects of ineffective and inefficient outputs on any PLC instance on their daily lives. So does a PLC mature and evolve moving from right to left because the downstream recipients want to change the future of the next PLC instance? As the Danish philosopher and theologian Søren Kierkegaard once said "Life can only be understood backwards, but it must be lived forwards." Let us now examine how a life cycle could be implemented and continuously improved, by rigorously learning from the past and applying it to the future.

Chapter 1

The First Failures

*Honesty is casting bright light on your own experience; Truth is casting it
on the experiences of all.*

—Anna Quindlen

Every day people get dressed, sharpen their pencils, and come to work
to solve problems. This book is about how a product life cycle, or PLC,
could be useful in solving a certain set of problems. Organizations respond to
pain and confusion. Change agents implementing a PLC can take advantage
of organizational pain if they illuminate the way forward by providing a vision,
answer the "what-do-I-need-to-do-differently?" question, and don't cost more
than the organization is willing to pay. However, even if one of the change
attributes is missing, the PLC implementation and expected results are lost.

The Paradox

From May of 1991 to June of 1997 the supercomputer systems division of
Intel Corporation built arguably the world's fastest computer four different
times. To be clear, this was not the same computer four times, but four unique
instances of the fastest computer.

These development efforts were accomplished without an agreed-to product life cycle for the first two years and with a new and not well understood life cycle for the last two. In general the workforce was well motivated to put together massively parallel high performance computing systems and many counted those years as some of the best in their careers. So why, with these accomplishments, did this division need, or even want, a product life cycle?

The answer is because everything was way harder than it needed to be.

It was more difficult because occasionally prototype material made it into the production system and was specified to contain a rare earth element that was not obtainable. It was because last-minute engineering change orders came in with the only rationale for the change being, "it was Tuesday." Then again it was the final integration and installation technicians who had to make do with under-evaluated systems and subsystems. With a scope and copious numbers of spare parts, they "loved" their systems all the way through customer acceptance. And this was just manufacturing.

When you traced it all the way back up the product development food chain it was a similar story. The Validation Team did under-evaluate because the Design Team slipped their schedules, even though the ship date did not. And Design wasn't having all that much fun reconciling the ambiguous and misleading requirements coming out of Architecture and Planning, which really didn't matter because Marketing was promising something completely different to the customer anyway. Then Management showed up at all the wrong times. They weren't there in the planning phase when key decisions were made, but when things went bad late in development and production phases, Management was there listening ineffectually to things they could not influence.

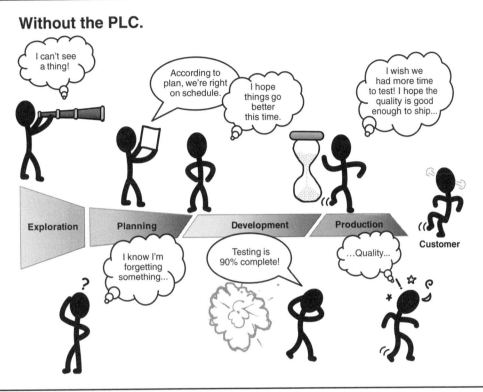

Figure 1.1   Product Development without a Documented, Agreed-to Life Cycle

Source: Adapted from PLC Promotion 2001

In the midst of this division's start-up mentality with all of its *esprit de corps* there emerged a need for a defined, documented product development and delivery system. Product launch commitments were consistently missed and de-featured, product quality was below customer expectations, and the costs of development, as well as the cost of the manufactured product, were above expectations. Management began to recognize the "cowboy methods[1]" by which products were defined and developed as a problem.

---

1   "Cowboy methods" compared to "team work" and collaboration, which is essential for product development. A *cowboy* describes someone who is reckless or ignores potential risks, is irresponsible, or who heedlessly handles a sensitive or dangerous task.

Justin Rattner – Intel Fellow 1994. *"Parallel Machines up to about 1991 had been relatively small and sold to research organizations where access to this kind of computing hardware was the essence of their activity. Computer science departments and government research labs were saying this is a different kind of computer. We need to learn how to use them. Delta was the crossover point. It was this really big machine. It was arguably the fastest in the world. It was a machine of such scale that we began to realize we weren't a hobby computer division. If SSD [Supercomputer Systems Division] had remained a boutique business that catered to computer science, algorithmic research, and other arcane disciplines, then we might not have thought about adopting a life cycle model, but when you are talking about machines that are tens and eventually hundreds of millions of dollars, you can't come in the morning and say well, what are we going to do today?"*

In 1994, the organization commissioned a PLC team to define a framework around which basic capabilities and methods could be repeated and/or improved.

Creating the Framework

The foundation for the PLC came from benchmarking studies from both Sun Microsystems and Sequent; books such as *Revolutionizing Product Development* by Wheelwright and Clark; and previous product development processes within Intel.

Dirk Werhane – Production Manager 1994. *"Back then we were selling big complex supercomputer systems to people that actually used them. These were people like the National Security Agency, Los Alamos National Labs, the Science and Engineering Research Centre, and California Institute of Technology. As the production manager I was directly responsible for making it happen. We integrated and tested the systems on our manufacturing floor before installing them and gaining acceptance at the customer site.*

Everything had to come together when we integrated our systems. The cabinetry, hardware, operating system, and the rest of the software all had to come together. It all came together haphazardly and we were typically late. The PLC project was an attempt to synchronize product development so that we could integrate the various parts of the system in a more predictable way.

I was part of the benchmarking visit to Sun Microsystems in the early nineties. Of interest to me was the big iron test they were doing down there. We had already started early work on a development cycle, but we did not know where it was going to go. They showed us their model. Across the top of the page was their funnel running from left to right dividing the funnel into phases. The functional organization ran down the left hand side of the page as 'swim lanes.' Under each phase the functional organizations put their key activities and milestones. Conceptually this gave us a good place to start."

At Intel the PLC took the form of a sideways funnel broken into phases with entry and exit points defined by a mix of documents and events. The funnel shape has changed somewhat over the years and has acquired various nicknames such as "the sideways rocket ship" and "the screw." The PLC looked like a phase gate process, but was always assumed to be a framework; the framework allows you to orient and synchronize the work of various functional swim lanes to commonly understood milestones.

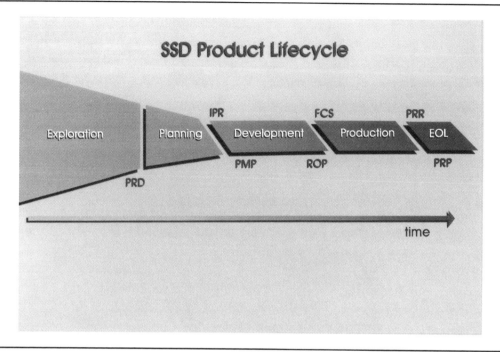

Figure 1.2   First Intel Product Life Cycle Created by the Supercomputer Systems Division (SSD) in 1994–1995

The PLC was meant to represent the convergence of market and technology forces that defined an opportunity so consistent with the product roadmap and so implementable it was moved into planning. In the planning phase, you find out what you didn't know you didn't know. In planning the product is scoped, feasibility determined, and committed to as the plan of record (POR). In the development phase the product is designed, verified, validated, and qualified for release into the marketplace where it is produced and eventually discontinued ("end-of-life'd").

With the high level structure, the framework, in place, then the attention turned to defining the detailed exit criteria for the milestones events and the content for the documents. The PLC team was responsible for the creating those details. Going from undocumented tribal knowledge to something agreed to and written down was not easy.

Rick East – Materials Planner 1994. *"I was new at Intel as a materials planner having come from Tandem, another large computer manufacturer. I had experience with life cycles and wanted to help this new Intel supercomputer project.*

We started first by putting together the phases of the PLC and that seemed to come together pretty well, except we thought we needed something before planning so we added an exploration phase even though we really didn't know what we would do in that phase.

We had a difficult time figuring out the exit criteria for each phase. We knew what we wanted, but it was a little too conceptual."

Dirk Werhane: *"We had difficulty because the devil was in the details. We were doing this in our spare time when we were working pretty much all the time getting product designed, built, and shipped.*

Our biggest detriment was setting aside quality time to do this detailed work. It was difficult doing all this work by function and integrating it all together. At the time concurrent engineering wasn't working at all. We basically were just slamming into each other."

For the rest of 1994 and all through 1995 the PLC team worked to flesh out the first documented PLC. The supercomputer division merged with a server start-up division and they were thereafter known colloquially as servers. By the end of that year the documented server PLC was in a nifty three-inch binder with a silkscreen logo on the cover and preprinted divider tabs containing a PowerPoint[†] presentation of the process, a glossary of terms that were new or changed, an annotated flowchart of the proposed process, documented templates key to the process, and a checklist to aid conformance to how the process "should" work. As it was rolled out in 1995 it ended up like many first time PLCs. It failed.

Why It Failed

Essentially the first PLC framework didn't work for those that developed products. The effort was largely a "push" by process quality. The training material was too conceptual. It was a description of an idealized state, not one achievable in a finite period of time. Attempts to conform to the milestone reviews were arduous, all-day affairs requiring significant preparation time. There was a perception that the PLC was getting in the way of development. The organizational antibodies in the server division began to activate. The PLC was referred to as onerous. A definition of onerous is "having legal obligations that outweigh the advantages." That of course is a problem.

Rick East – *"People at the time viewed the PLC as bureaucratic roadblocks getting in the way of product development.*

The PLC was started for good reasons, but it was like wet clay and forming that was useful, but it was…hard. It was hard because it was not part of the Intel culture, it was hard because it was new, and it was hard because 'they' did not believe in it."

Besides the tactical errors, there was a larger, more fundamental reason the first attempt at a PLC failed; namely middle management. That would be the *"they"* mentioned above. To create change, to truly be a change agent, requires moving middle management into an unsettled state so that a new, and presumably improved, status quo can be defined and diffused throughout the organization. However, middle managers were the ones who defined and maintained the status quo on how things got done; the PLC challenged their status quo.

It's important to understand that implementing the PLC is about knowing when change is possible and how to put enablers in place so change is possible. Anyone doing this type of work must examine their role as a change agent. They must continue to purposefully develop a competency around understanding how to create change *in the partner organizations* to deliver something that works for them.

Creating Change

As Figure 1.3 suggests, change is possible when there is a sufficient amount of organizational pain or discomfort with the status quo, when there is a pretty clear vision of what the new status quo looks like, and the steps to get there are defined. Change is possible if all three elements are in place, and are greater than the cost of change. These elements are the enablers of change. A change agent knows how to act when these conditions exist and how to enable those conditions when they don't exist. This concept is not new. Different words are used to convey the just about the same idea in Dennis Pawley's foreword to *A Hitchhiker's Guide to Lean.*

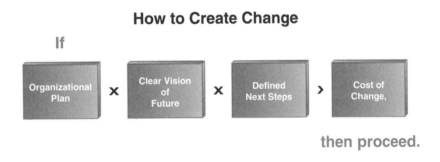

How to Create Change

Figure 1.3 The Change Formula *Source "The Implementation of the Product Lifecycle at Intel" – Galluzzo 2002*

Not understanding the relationship between the elements of the Change Formula killed the first PLC. The reason for failure was not a lack of organizational pain; the division knew it had a problem and wanted to change. The PLC's clear vision of the future was very consistent with product development models of the early nineties, but the vision was not communicated in a way that middle management could understand it. The value proposition was a mystery to them. But the most significant issue was the lack of clearly defined next steps that were palatable for the maturity of the organization. Not knowing "how to do" the thing they didn't understand killed the forward momentum. The PLC was therefore not relevant to the people that actually did product development. It did not work for them.

The organizational pain was still there so the division tried again with a different approach.

Lessons Learned

- The attributes of the Change Formula help the change agent define when a change is possible or when it is not. If even one attribute is missing, then the result is usually failure.

- Frameworks or processes that cost more than their intended value will be ignored.

Questions

1. What is making my product development system "too hard"?

2. Can I benchmark other companies for their product development frameworks?

3. Can I borrow an existing framework and adapt it to my business?

4. What pressures (crises) in my environment are causing "organizational pain"?

Chapter 2

A Timely Crisis

May you live in interesting times.

—Purported Chinese Curse

A t the end of 1995, while the server group was rolling out its first failed attempt at a PLC, the rapidly growing desktop motherboard group and its associated manufacturing operation were dealing with their own set of issues. This would turn out to be a rather substantial dose of organizational pain.

A Bad Day to Come into the Office

In 1995 Mike Neal transferred within Intel from his long-term job in marketing to a position titled Manager of Manufacturing Quality. This was in support of Intel's growing motherboard factories. In later years Mike would remark that the only reason he got the job was he knew how to talk to customers. Part of his new job was to go out and talk to customers and figure out what was going on.

At the same time, Peggy Kessinger was the Quality Engineering Manager for the division developing desktop motherboards. This division was essentially a start-up within Intel only a few years before. As recently as 1993, the division had sweatshirts printed with the tag line: "Out of Control and Loving It."

Peggy's job was to drive quality processes within the "out of control and loving it" product development division in support of a reduction in motherboard defects per million (DPM).

The relationship between product development and manufacturing was antagonistic. Manufacturing believed they could build great products if only the products were designed so they could build them. Design thought Manufacturing couldn't build a damn thing. But these two divergent perspectives didn't matter after November of 1995 when Andy Grove, Intel CEO, paid a visit to Michael Dell, the founder and CEO of Dell Computing. With a customer perceived line fallout of 30,000 DPM, Michael informed Andy that Intel was his worst board supplier. Andy, a self-proclaimed "man of action," returned from that meeting to initiate corrective action inside Intel. The "corrective action" began at the Hawthorn Farms desktop development site in Hillsboro, Oregon in the campus main cafeteria.

Mike Neal – Manager of Manufacturing Quality 1995 *"It was in the café and that's important because he (Andy Grove) got the whole building. Fifteen hundred people in the café. When the CEO comes up just like that and says "Everybody in the cafeteria—I want to talk to you," it wasn't attend if you feel like it, it was every warm body right down to the tech's on the line.*

It was an interesting exercise in leadership. He employed two different people. The one in the café where he was cool and calm. Andy talked eloquently about the importance of quality and Intel's history with quality and how we have learned this before. We have made these mistakes but quality is important.

And then there was another meeting with the head of product development, manufacturing, and a few other managers including myself. Andy was eloquent in a different way. He was angry and he let the heat show. There was no ambiguity. He wanted it fixed. Money was not an object, but money wasn't the answer. We didn't know what was broken."

The way forward was not clear or easy. They had nothing to talk about at the end of 1995 because they lacked customer data. For Intel boards and systems divisions this was an attribute of the time. The quality systems in this part of the business had for the most part been dismembered during the industry recession of the mid-eighties. When the market started to recover, that support infrastructure was far behind in resources and maturity. The boards and systems businesses that survived or were born in that timeframe were largely cowboy engineering start-ups.

Peggy Kessinger – Quality Engineering Manager 1995 *"While it was true that we had a general manager who was fond of saying 'out of control and loving it,' the reason for it was the environment at the time was innovation. So you have to think of that general manager as an entrepreneur who was pushing the envelope from the perspective of design innovation. From his perspective... process be damned...get it into the product and out the door. He was really good at finding very creative people, just like entrepreneurs are, and he had a charismatic way about him that would help people rise to their best capabilities. And it happened. It wasn't just 'out of control and loving it,' it was thinking outside the box and we needed that environment to get the innovation. We were super successful. Ten million boards in 1995 and our quality sucked...and then we got "religion."*

One of the first "religious" experiences happened with the resident engineering program, which started in the end of 1995. Six sustaining engineers were assigned for six months and deployed at all the major customer sites. From a marketing point of view the objective was to get the customer calmed down, but the more fundamental objective was to get the verified customer data back to Intel. It was the start of a much needed feedback system.

Help came from corporate management. Intel's silicon manufacturing capability was a well-oiled machine and the engineering to manufacturing handoff equally structured and predictable. Craig Barrett, who was the COO at the time, came regularly to review the system and process health. The reviews were brutal as they uncovered systems that were either nonexistent or merely ad hoc at best. Boards and systems were the land of process lawlessness.

Mike Neal – *"We did these monthly operations reviews with Barrett. I can still picture him sitting in the middle of the auditorium as I spoke. 'You are showing an amazing amount of competence' he remarked in the middle of our presentation. All of us had been throwing slides together as we were in present-for-survival mode and Barrett was smart enough to pick up on some the discrepancies between our slides."*

The monthly operations reviews became the forcing function to drive the data, or lack of data out into the open. Motivation to show improvement, with consistent data, operations review to operations review, became very clear. The resident engineering program feedback system allowed for this improvement.

Remember to Feed the Feedback System

With the resident engineer program and the focus from the operations reviews and the focus on statistical trending, the feedback systems improved and reliable data was becoming available so that systematic problem solving could occur. This proved to be the necessary foundation to continue the corrective action.

Peggy Kessinger – *"And then there was Mike who internalized and perfected the feedback system and data trends so that we would have data we could trust. Up to that point there was a lot of finger pointing. Honestly, before that we did not have a feedback system. He was the perfect person coming from Marketing. Well anyway, he set up the process. Before that we had no data. It was manufacturing screaming because they were getting beat up by customers, but we had no data."*

Mike Neal – *"So the numbers, the 30,000 DPM, came from Dell because that was what Michael said their internal three percent line fallout was and a lot of that was them damaging the product. But that was the only data we had; how could we argue with that? So we collected data and found it was more like 10,000 DPM and then we started working it down. You know Dell's goal was 1000 DPM. There were a lot of arguments about internal goals."*

One thousand DPM was a pretty audacious goal given where desktop motherboards were, but the target was clear enough from the customer perspective. With the feedback systems coming on line, the desktop people had what they needed to create a breakthrough system.

In Daniels and Mathers' book *ChangeABLE: Key Management Practices for Speed and Flexibility,* breakthrough systems are one of the five management practices.

A breakthrough system has three elements:

1. Clear expectation aligned to the team leader,

2. Each individual had a feedback system to check on progress towards the objective, and

3. Each individual had the resources to accomplish the objective.

In this case the expectation was clear: get to 1000 DPM. Many thought it impossible, but the goal was clear. The missing link was the feedback system that was put in place during this timeframe. Andy had already said he would write the checks to get this fixed so the resourcing was there as well. It would take time, but a breakthrough system was coming together in 1996.

From the "How to Create Change" formula in the first chapter of this book, you can find all the "necessary" elements for creating change in the Desktop board customer issue, as shown in Figure 2.1. There was clearly *organizational pain*. The meeting between Michael Dell and Andy Grove in November of 1995 took care of that. There was a *clear vision of the future*. Get your customer line fallout problems fixed and the goal was 1000 DPM. And finally there were *defined next steps,* which were to make incremental improvement supported by statistically valid data before Barrett's next operational review.

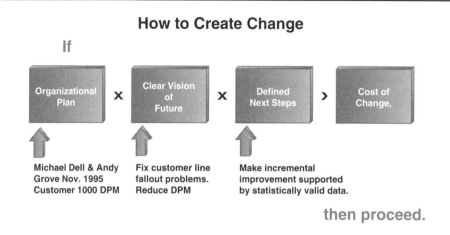

Figure 2.1   How to Create Change

Here were all the elements needed to create change and build a breakthrough system. By the middle of 1996 things were going in the right direction and that is when desktops took notice of the PLC. Servers released a retooled version in May of 1996. Desktops saw this as an opportunity to better align their feedback systems so that customer feedback went to manufacturing and manufacturing feedback went to design. It was also an opportunity to synchronize on milestones and set expectations. Desktops decided to create their own PLC, so in 1996 going into 1997 the two PLCs were in parallel universes. Desktops' first PLC version was arguably just as onerous as servers' first PLC attempt.

Peggy Kessinger – *"It was in the second half of 1996 that the PLC became so onerous. It became onerous because of these monthly reviews with Barrett. We were throwing everything in but the kitchen sink to prove to him that we knew what we were doing when we didn't have a clue."*

Sarah Nesland – Materials Program Manager 1996 *"As part of the manufacturing team we needed to come up with all of the data for the PLC decision meetings. The decision meetings were far and few between! We amassed a large amount of data to make a decision, which everyone had to plow through and it just felt onerous. You didn't have the essence of the information you really needed to know and you had all this extraneous stuff. The whole team felt weighted down when the expectation was to move fast and get the motherboards to the factory and ramp. I think this first version in Desktop forced a big overhaul as a result of how the team felt."*

So you learn what you have to learn when it is time to learn it. What did they learn? Feedback systems are critical, but sifting through all the data to feed the feedback system with the information that is vital is the only way to make the system, and the PLC, useful.

Tom Rampone – Engineering Manager 1996 *"You reach a level of complexity where you need a framework like the PLC. It is the structure around which we put our processes in place under which we do work and find ways to communicate with each other effectively to avoid confusion and misunderstanding. But if anything, I would err on the side of being a little bit too light. It really comes down to knowing what your team's collective experience is. A team with three or four cycles under the belt needs much less rigorous or exhausted process oversight than one that is going through it for the first or second time."*

While servers saw the retooled PLC as an improvement, they had other more pressing issues; they had customer line fallout issues too. Only theirs was not a 30,000 DPM issue, but rather a 100,000 DPM issue. One out of 10 server boards failed on the customer line. Big problem! This time the weight of the experienced and mature part of corporate Intel landed on boards and systems. There was much to be done with basic quality systems. Boards and systems were roughly a billion-dollar set of businesses without the process and infrastructure necessary for an appropriate quality system.

Mike Neal – *"Gerry Parker, co-leader of the technology and manufacturing group, was up for numerous reviews. After one review he scheduled a half-day with me just to help me with our approach to quality. It was the basics, but it kept me from jumping off the side of the building."*

That was the start of building a quality system within Intel boards and systems and the PLC would be part of that system. Piece by piece over a period of many months, the boards and systems quality system came together. Ironically, much of the learning in boards and systems from this time would eventually influence change across the more mature and established businesses within Intel.

If there was an evolution analogy relating to process maturity of server and desktop organizations from that time it would be this: two primitive life-form organizations, desktop and server motherboards, would emerge crawling from a primordial sea and become aware of each other's existence. After wondering for some period of time if they should eat or be eaten they both concluded the same thing: maybe they could help each other out.

Could the two divisions, two unique product types, use the same high-level PLC framework? Would one common PLC function for both Intel internal product development and our customer's quality requirements?

Lessons Learned

- Organizational pain comes in many forms; the key is how to use it to your advantage.
- As the product development system becomes more complex, the need to simplify and clearly articulate "next steps" becomes more urgent.
- Feedback systems are a critical element in breakthrough system.

Questions

1. How does my company simplify even our most complex product development systems at the top level?

2. Do my pain points equal "organizational" pain, is there a clear vision for the future, and do I know the needed next steps?

3. Does my organization have all three elements necessary to create a breakthrough system?

Chapter 3

Turnaround

The demon that you can swallow gives you its power, and the greater life's pain, the greater life's reply.

— Joseph Campbell

Through the back end of 1996 and into 1997 corporate Intel was providing process and system life support to the desktop and server divisions for a wide range of basic capabilities. Management tracked progress via a dashboard that showed weak, broken, or nonexistent capabilities. The overhaul included such things as post-release change control, product qualification, material qualification, and new product introduction (NPI). The need for a PLC that would stick was one of those capabilities. It served as a framework, a synchronization tool, to help orient the other capabilities. This time the server and desktop divisions came together to create the next revision of the PLC and with lessons learned from earlier failed attempts.

Raising the PLC Bar

Through the art of compromise the two divisions hammered out a PLC revision not only acceptable to both, but also an acknowledged improvement over previous attempts. With the two divisions in agreement there was sufficient momentum to engage the early adopters of the PLC at Intel. PLC Rev 2.0 is shown in Figure 3.1.

Peggy Kessinger – *"We created a PLC forum. What I remember is we had a meeting in Hawthorn Farm and Servers came over and presented their PLC. We talked about ours. We were arguing for months. We had some crazy milestones, but over time a few ended up sticking and we came up with agreed-upon terms and the exit criteria for them. We published our joint PLC in May of 1997."*

PLC Rev. 2.0

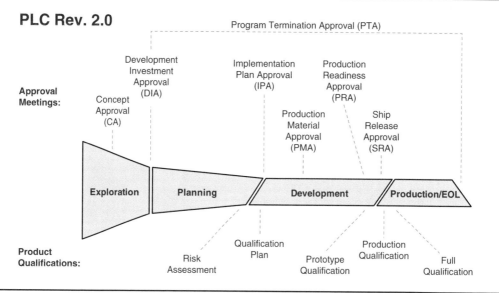

Figure 3.1   Product Life Cycle, Revision 2.0
Source: Intel Product Life Cycle, Revision 2.0 – 1997

While focused primarily on the engineering to manufacturing handoff, there were several improvements to the framework. The approval milestones were above the PLC funnel. The supporting documentation used to make the approval decision was below the PLC funnel. The content description, audience, and intended purpose were detailed in the supporting documentation whereas intent, exit criteria, and decision responsibility were defined in the approval milestone. Discussions and arguments at this level of detail associated with each acronym on the PLC kicked the maturity of the Revision 2 release to an improved level.

In the exploration phase timeframe, there were unauthorized "good idea" projects running around sucking up resources that needed to be focused on the officially authorized projects. The remedy was addition of an approval decision, Concept Approval or CA, in the late exploration phase. The behavior change intended was a focus of resources on a managed set of "good ideas" that had gone through the CA decision process with the appropriated business partners.

The first milestone at the beginning of the planning phase, Development Investment Approval or DIA, represented an emotional commitment of the division to fund the project through the rest of the life cycle. At this milestone the project would move from an internal roadmap to an external roadmap, which increased the risk and cost if the project was killed.

Projects in the planning phase would require defined and formal steps to cancel or appreciably change a project's goals, requirements, or expected outcomes. Throughout the planning phase a development organization figured out all the items they "didn't know they didn't know," and put plans in place to solve what they now knew they did not know. The milestone at the end of the planning phase, Implementation Plan Approval or IPA, was the organization's commitment to the various design, verification, validation, and quality aspects of the development phase. This committed the organization to its plan of record.

In the development and production phases, the PLC's usefulness as an orientation or synchronization tool was tested. The two organizations started associating other processes with the life cycle, for example, Qualification Processes (specifications) and Plan of Record Change Control. These supporting processes were associated all along the development phase milestones ending with evidence that the product was qualified ahead of the Ship Release Approval meeting or SRA, the decision to ship the product for revenue.

The two divisions also collaborated to produce training collateral providing different levels of detail for different audiences. If some needed rationale for adopting the PLC, or the details of each exit criteria, or what exactly do you want me to do differently, the flexible training material adapted to the audience. A big difference from the Revision 1.0 attempt was the method employed by the motherboard division to deploy this revision of the PLC and catalyze adoption.

Digestible Deployment

Peggy Kessinger – *"We had another general manager back then who made his expectations very clear. He was fond of saying 'what gets measured is what gets done.' He made it clear we would have a common PLC between the two divisions and that we would follow those agreed-upon milestones. He said he would not tell us how we would navigate the milestones, but we would follow them. He set the expectation, but then he stayed out of the details. He wanted the measurement and challenged his organization to figure out the 'how' part together."*

The quality department, lead by Peggy Kessinger, used the PLC Forum as a way to create tools and templates to support adoption and usage of the milestones. The output was shared cooperatively with the program managers.

Peggy Kessinger – *"When it came to implementing the PLC, I used the program managers. They were the implementers of the framework. They had their feet held to the fire by the 'what gets measured is what gets done' management style. We would provide low overhead tools and templates to help navigate the milestone. Together we would agree which project would take the lead and experiment with the new tool. After the milestone, we would review how the navigation went and make improvements for the next project that approached the milestone. We made improvements quickly and the PLC became part of the culture."*

The program managers defined the content for approval meetings. They differentiated between approval meeting and peer reviews at pre-determined synchronization points (life cycle milestones). The PLC Forum gave latitude to the program managers to choose documentation format and content, as long as neither violated the intent of the milestone. The PLC Forum examined every milestone with the intention of creating a standardized template for each. The output of this activity returned to the program managers for use on future programs. This new approach was echoed by the engineering manager, Tom Rampone.

Tom Rampone – *"The new general manager had a reputation of coming down hard on execution and predictability; different than previous leadership with the "try hard, run fast" attitude, who was more understanding of missteps. The new leadership set the expectations, but did not tell people how to navigate the milestones. The PLC was treated as a framework that needed to evolve. This tone from leadership allowed it to succeed."*

"One of the innovations we evolved was planning and execution toward defined 'success criteria.' These were negotiated elements of program success defined before the end of the planning phase. At the end of the day 'what does the product need to be?' The wrong way is making up the criteria as the team nears a milestone. The PLC is a great way to set expectations."

The PLC Forum provided a structure for anyone in the organization to submit product development ideas and a means to share ideas between development programs. The program managers took each milestone template from the PLC Forum and decided which program was best suited to experiment with the template. Participation was voluntary. The results of the experiments were fed back to the PLC Forum. Figure 3.2 shows the symbiotic relationship between the PLC team and program managers.

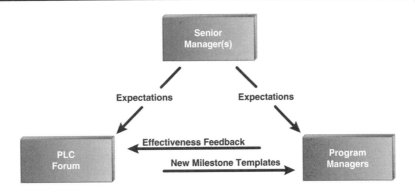

Figure 3.2   Relationship between the PLC Forum, the Program Managers, and the Senior Managers' Expectations. *Source: "The Implementation of the Product Lifecycle at Intel" – Galluzzo 2002.*

The bottom line was the process people (PLC Forum) and the getting-it-done people (program managers) started working together to do something different with the correct level of process. By taking evolutionary baby steps towards an agreed-upon standard, the organizational learning and change happened. These efforts supported senior managers' expectations to meet the PLC intent.

From this interactive relationship, useful tools and techniques began to appear. Collateral was produced for all conference room walls. Individual identification badge attachments were produced. Functional middle managers were drafted to conduct training in workgroups. Training was conducted in teams of two to ensure correct delivery of the PLC concepts. The examination, experimentation, and final adoption of each PLC milestone continued through 1997. Each iteration of the milestone templates brought clarification to milestone purpose and necessary content, based on its purpose.

Toward the end of 1997, the finance organization introduced hurdle-rates to the PLC. During the PLC exploration and planning phases, financial expectations, or "hurdles," were defined. The risk of not achieving these financial expectations had to decrease to prescribed levels as the programs moved from one approval meeting at the left of the funnel to the next approval meeting to the right. This technique efficiently helped to cull weaker proposals earlier in the PLC. Both finance and program management were key in this phase of implementation. They were the two organizations that ultimately determined if the PLC improved business results.

The desktop motherboard division figured out the adoption technique on their own via trial and error. And upon reflection, this approach was corroborated by literature, for example Edger Schein's two principles related to balancing survival anxiety with learning anxiety.[1]

Survival anxiety comes from sufficient disconfirmation data that the status quo is not working (organizational pain) coupled with specific direction from management on milestone expectations (clear vision). To survive in the organization you had to change and meet the new expectation.

---

1   *The Corporate Culture Survival Guide,* Edgar H. Schein, Jossey-Bass Publishers (San Francisco; 1999), pages 121–123.

The opposing fear to survival anxiety is *learning anxiety,* which comes when you have to unlearn something and learn something new (defined next steps). These are basic fears like being temporarily incompetent and the real or imagined fear of punishment for this incompetence. It could also be the fear of loss of personal identity in the old status quo or loss of group membership. These are the anxieties to balance. In doing so you must balance Schein's two principles:

■ Principle One: Survival anxiety or guilt must be greater than learning anxiety.

■ Principle Two: Learning anxiety must be reduced rather than increasing survival anxiety.

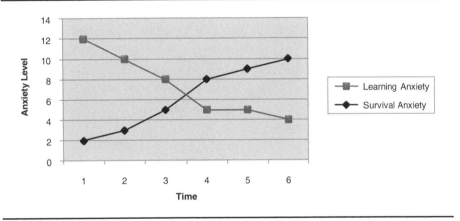

Figure 3.3 Survival versus Learning Anxiety Crossover Point

The desktop motherboard organization experienced both. There was enough disconfirmation and specific management expectation to create appropriate survival anxiety. The deal struck between the PLC Forum and the program managers allowed the transformational change to happen at a digestible, nonthreatening pace (clear next steps).

Some of the specific "things" that desktop people developed were:

■ A compelling positive vision

■ Formal training

■ Involvement of the learner

■ Informal training of relevant "family" groups and teams

■ Practice fields, coaches, and feedback

■ Positive role models

■ Support groups

■ Consistent systems and structures

Note: All of these are in Schein's list of suggestions to create psychological safety.

The server division was not as effective in creating a nonthreatening forum to drive change nor was it as successful in setting clear management expectation. Even though both divisions were able to create an environment for change, the desktop division was more successful in getting business results as the management expectations were crystal clear and they had better feedback mechanisms.

Tom Rampone – *"Those feedback systems were initially postproduction as we were trying to get feedback on units that Dell was consuming and having trouble with. Eventually in preproduction we began to have some notion of whether we were on track or not. We caught defects and root-caused them in our early builds that led up to production. So it affected the backend of the PLC both preproduction as well as postproduction. Some of the data came all the way back to design for best known methods to make more robust designs."*

As the PLC was being deployed and adopted, the other processes associated with the life cycle were also being deployed with measurable success. The first-ever release of the boards and systems product qualification specification began successfully qualifying products prior to shipment for revenue improving the quality of handoff between design and manufacturing and the ultimate shipment to the customer.

The creation of this boards and systems product qualification specification was done in partnership with the established silicon qualification experts. New techniques were piloted in the boards and systems specification that would have been more difficult to introduce in the traditional silicon qualification specification, which had gotten stale. The successful existence proof of these new techniques led to an overhaul of the corporate product qualification system that would now include boards and systems.

Post-release change management practices were adopted and fixed basic issues in the production phase, such as change control boards, proper customer notification, and product segregation in the warehouse. As in the example of product qualification, corporate change management took notice and partnered with boards and systems to make companywide improvements.

It was in this timeframe the horizontal organizations (organizations that supported many business units) began to use the PLC to influence the vertical, "stove-piped" product development organizations.

Leveraging the One-to-Many Organizations

Boards and systems manufacturing was one of these horizontal organizations. Their New Product Introduction (NPI) processes had to support everything from supercomputers to servers to desktop motherboards to laptop boards to add-in cards. All of the processes from these various divisions were not only different, but needlessly so. Using the now accepted PLC as the common framework; manufacturing influenced a common NPI process across boards and systems.

Sarah Nesland – *"Tugrul Daim and I were transferred into Manufacturing and our charter was to standardize on the detailed transfer process across all of the board factories and business groups. The lack of standardization was hurting our factory efficiency. We used the PLC because everyone related to it and we embedded the standardized manufacturing process into the PLC."*

By leveraging the horizontal organization, all three elements of change agency are in play. Organizations, such as manufacturing, that span many business units benefit from consistency. Business units strive for autonomy. Horizontal organizations put tension in the system that creates organizational pain. Then, working together with the business units, horizontal organizations help define a clear vision of the future and work to define next steps to implement what they have jointly defined. This approach dramatically increases the number or resources driving transformative change. This also helped influence the adoption of the PLC from its desktop and server base to the rest of the boards and systems product divisions.

In August of 1997 Mike Neal received an award at Dell presented to him personally by Michael Dell for quality improvements made over a two-year period. There was a subsequent e-mail message from Michael Dell to Andy Grove letting him know of this award in acknowledgement of the improvements that had been made.

Mike Neal – *"I got a lot of plaques in my career. Most are good for firewood, but I kept the one from Dell. As far as Dell was concerned it took us two years to get from 30,000 DPM to 2000. In order to frame things it took us two years to effectively solve our engineering to manufacturing quality problems. We were actually able to design and build boards that would run on our lines and be tested to what the customer actually did with them. One of the things we put in place along with the PLC was the concept of quality actually signing off on the ship release. So as much as you have this PLC framework and it is cooperative, there are boundary conditions. The boundary condition was that if the quality manager or somebody else did not agree that this product was ready to ship, then it did not ship."*

With the PLC deployed and adopted and several engineering to manufacturing practices also deployed, it was time to move left in fleshing out the PLC. All that was needed was another crisis opportunity.

Lessons Learned

- Clear management expectations coupled with a symbiotic relationship between the support people and the product people leads to increased adoption of change.
- Balancing survival anxiety with learning anxiety increases the chances for successful adoption of change.

Questions

1. How is "commitment" to plans made in your organization?
2. Are expectations for product development set and communicated "before execution" begins?
3. Are multiple perspectives represented in the definition and adoption of changes?

Chapter 4

Breakthrough

Sometimes a breakdown can be the beginning of a kind of breakthrough, a way of living in advance through a trauma that prepares you for a future of radical transformation.

—Cherrie Moraga

It is 1998, the PLC is now adopted in two divisions and manufacturing is influencing the expansion of the PLC in other boards and systems divisions. The PLC had potential for deployment across the broader Intel, but it was not yet ready for expansion as it lacked broad credibility. By then Mike Neal was responsible for quality in the majority of boards and systems business units working for the Corporate Quality Network (CQN), which had tentacles throughout the company.

Mike Neal – *"Back in 1996 Toshiba sent their director of quality to live in Hawthorn Farm for six weeks. So basically every single morning at 8:00 I had to meet with him and every single morning I got asked the same question: 'Mike, what is your quality system?' And the problem was we didn't have a quality system. He came back in 1998 and we talked about the PLC. He reflected that we actually had a quality system now. It wasn't an entire quality system, but at least the PLC was a robust component of a quality system."*

By 1998 Mike saw that many of the design-to-manufacturing handoff problems were behind him. He began openly talking to his boss about CQN assuming sponsorship for the PLC. At this time the PLC moved into CQN, but in the midst of these discussions Mike had yet another problem to deal with.

I Seem to Recall that Recall

What Intel thought would be a smooth ramp-up for its chipset/motherboard in 1998 and 1999 turned into a motherboard product recall costing hundreds of millions of dollars and a black eye for the company.

Mike Neal – *"We had solved the manufacturing quality and interface to the product division problems, and now the characteristics of our quality problem started to change to more systematic issues in design that impacted all units. This was the kind of quality problem that drove us to swim upstream in product development. How do you stop this type of excursion?"*

Peggy Kessinger – *"There were three chips in that chipset. The defect was in one of those chipsets, but we could have designed it out at the board level. It was the way we designed the board that made the problem happen. There were these errata in the chipset that the board design exacerbated somehow and then everything blew up. It turns out there were also other customers that also had the problem we had. It wasn't just us that designed it and exacerbated the problem."*

In their book The Management and Control of Quality, Fifth Edition Evans and Lindsey cite in the preface the Intel board recall of 1998 as one of many infamous examples that quality problems still abound. In this crisis the out-of-control element was the design. This recall originated from a design bug in an obscure corner of the design envelope that was not detected in a very manual validation and qualification process. Again, a crisis provides motivation for change. This time the issue wasn't with the backend where design hands off to manufacturing, but in the design space, where design quality is determined by how well you define requirements.

The objective for improvement shifted from late in the development phase upstream in the life cycle to design quality and requirements, both design and product qualification. The planning and early development phase improvements needed to be documented more completely as part of the next revision of the PLC. This included other processes and capabilities that would be hung on the PLC framework. Just as product qualification and change management were associated with the late development phase, requirements, document inspections, and upfront quality plans needed to be documented earlier in the lifecycle. These next sets of improvements were, in part, catalyzed by the recall. As compared to the manufacturing instance in the previous chapter, this would prove a more profound example of leveraging the one-to-many horizontal organizations.

Enter the Software Dragon

In 1998 Intel ranked among the top five companies in the annual production of lines of commercial code. This included BIOS, drivers, tools, applications, and even an occasional operating system. Software was pervasive in every product at Intel so therefore across the company. There was a part of the CQN organization focused on software, logically titled SW CQN. They were chartered with establishing best practices, capabilities, and tools within the widespread software community.

The software community's first reaction to PLC was dismissive. Stage gate models are not known for their effectiveness in rapidly iterative forms of software development. To be fair, the PLC only looked like a stage gate process. In reality it is neither a "stage gate" nor a "process;" rather it is a "framework" as stated many times thus far. When members of the software community found out it was a framework capable of facilitating many forms of design and development methods they decided to take a closer look and then they decided to influence the next revision of the PLC in a big way.

In 1998, representatives from the software community joined the Intel Joint PLC Forum to document Revision 3.0 of the PLC. This rewrite was to encompass multiple Intel divisions/groups and merge hardware and software milestones into one Intel PLC reference procedure. There was a shadow team of software people creating a similar but much more detailed software PLC. That team was led by SW CQN. The two software representatives on the

PLC forum were also on the software shadow team. Their job was to make sure the best ideas coming out of the software PLC made its way into the corporate version. The input came in volumes and every word on every page of the rewrite was argued.

Bruce Clark – *Platform Program Manager 1998 "I was part of the team that drafted the combined Intel PLC. Both sides, hardware and software, were being very passionate and not wanting to give up perceived or actual control. There was lots of positioning, wordsmithing, and politics. Going over every word on every page for weeks was excruciating. What even made it more painful was that I hate process."*

Tom Rampone – *"I assumed the PLC forum would be heavy with process and software people. I didn't have the budget to go too crazy or too deep on process. I remembered thinking about putting someone on the forum that wanted to go fast. I asked one of my program managers, Bruce Clark, to be our representative to the forum. He thought I was crazy because he hated process. I told him that made him perfect, because if he signed his name to the document it meant it was actually useful to someone like him. In the end Bruce tempered the otherwise 'religious' element. I know I couldn't have all Bruces on the forum, but one Bruce and nine process/software types was about right."*

As painful as the intense wordsmithing and rework of the PLC Revision 3.0 was, the result was a clear and cohesive document. The milestones did not change as much as the clarity and flow of the content. Revision 3.0 added clarity on PLC success criteria, roles and responsibilities for deployment and adoption, and a more complete set of definitions, as well as more practical sequencing of events. Due in a large part to the software influence, the PLC Revision 3.0 put a greater focus on clear product requirements and document inspections to ensure the requirements were of high quality. This focus on requirements was the shift left in the PLC that was needed to get ahead of product definition.

Erik Simmons – *Requirements Engineering Program Manager 1999 "I was hired to influence requirements engineering in the software development community. Internal research work prior to my arrival elevated the requirements problem to enough altitude at Intel that they were even willing to think about a position to help fix it. As I joined Intel I found the need for clearer requirements was not limited to software. The need was pervasive across the company. Because of the environmental influences in this timeframe, there was a growing awareness that design quality was important."*

Because PLC Revision 3.0 was embraced by the software community PLC exposure and advocacy was viral, spreading the PLC fast and far, breaking out of boards and systems into mainstream silicon products. Posters with the life cycle appeared in conference rooms at Intel product development sites. Intel is a meeting-driven culture, so people from design, validation, program management, and so on naturally began to orient their work to the picture on the wall.

Key to Revision 3.0 was its relevance to the development community. Because it was practical as a tool to set expectations and make decisions, it got used. While it would be a few more years before the PLC was deployed across the entire company, the period of 1998 to 1999 was the highest rate of deployment and adoption for the PLC. In hindsight, the advocacy by the software community as well as the relevance to the product development environment of Revision 3.0 created the momentum for the PLC to win the early majority.

In Everett M. Rogers' book *Diffusion of Innovation* he describes the classic diffusion S curve, shown in Figure 4.1. To extend beyond the early adopters, key to gaining tipping point in any Innovation is winning the early majority. Rogers characterizes the early majority as deliberate.

"*The early majority adopt new ideas just before the average member of a system. The early majority interacts frequently with their peers, but seldom holds positions of opinion leadership in a system. The early majority's unique position between the very early and the relatively late to adopt makes them an important link in the diffusion process. They provide interconnectedness in the system's interpersonal networks. The early majority are the most numerous adopter categories, making up one third of the members of the system.*

The early majority may deliberate for some time before they completely adopt a new idea. Their innovation-decision period is relatively longer than that of the innovator and the early adopter. 'Be not the first by which new is tried, Nor the last to lay the old aside'; quoted at the top of the present chapter, particularly fits the thinking of the early majority. They follow with deliberate willingness in adopting innovations, but seldom lead."

Everett M. Rogers – *Diffusion of Innovation, Fourth Edition*

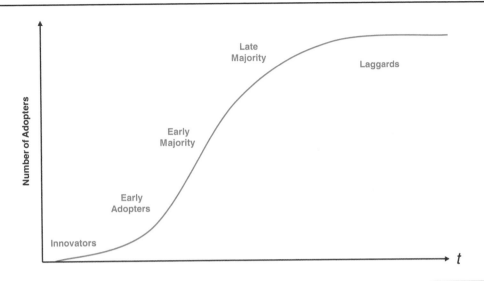

Figure 4.1   Diffusion of Innovation S Curve

Erik Simmons – *"Revision 3.0 of the PLC [Figure 4.2] transcended from an individual phenomenon to a group phenomenon. Individual organizations were adopting here and there, but with Revision 3.0 there came a tipping point affecting groups of organizations. In my mind software influenced the product called PLC revision 3.0, but it did not influence widespread adoption. Software groups were not powerful enough. However, their pervasiveness across the company gave them the opportunity to create awareness of the PLC to influence people who then saw the PLC as a way to solve a problem."*

Sarah Nesland – *"So for me what I remember was that all of a sudden the PLC gained this whole new level of formality, acceptance, depth, and richness that it never really had before. With that came a whole lot of different perspectives; like the desire to use it."*

PLC Rev. 3.0

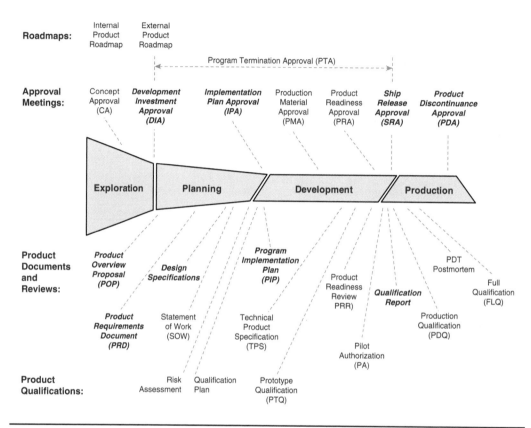

Figure 4.2   PLC Revision 3.0 *Source: Intel Product Life Cycle, Revision 3.0 – 1998*

And Now the Results, Please

During 1998–1999, the business groups that had adopted and used a PLC started to see the first tangible results. From their experience and corroborating industry data, an adoption benchmark emerged. In most instances, a business group needs one year to adopt the PLC and another year of usage to prove that it actually does some good for the business.

By the end of 1998, the desktop division found that a year-to-year comparison of product development efforts best told the story. While the following results are a combination of many factors, the implementation of the PLC was considered by desktop-motherboards division to be one of those factors. Figure 4.3 shows a decrease in Time-to-Money (TTM), while achieving improved development efficiency.

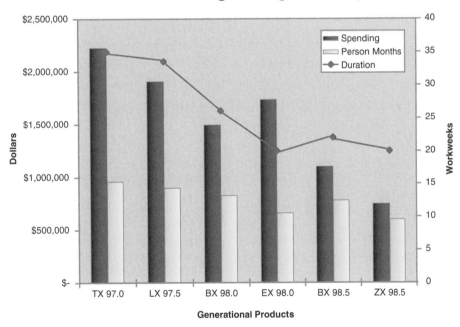

Figure 4.3   Generational Engineering Efficiency *Source: "The Implementation of the Product Lifecycle at Intel" – Galluzzo 2002*

As the adoption continued, so did the success stories, business unit after business unit. And as the success stories mounted so did the rate of adoption. As you will see in the next chapter, the diffusion of the PLC did follow the classic diffusion S curve. But to extend adoption to the late majority a structure to scale was needed and within that structure came the next set of improvements to the PLC.

Lessons Learned

■ Issues or gaps in the early phases tend to manifest themselves in the development or execution phases.

■ The life cycle alone is not the answer; life cycles in concert with other business processes yield business results.

Questions

1. Have you established the root cause of the issues and gaps in execution?

2. What existing networks within your organization could provide a vehicle for change? Can you influence a group of early adopters?

3. How quickly can your organization change directions within your business environment?

Chapter 5

Arrival

He who rejects change is the architect of decay. The only human institution which rejects progress is the cemetery.

—Harold Wilson

By 1999, the PLC was in deployment across increasing number of organizations at Intel, but as before the problem of the era was changing. Intel at the time was a diverse set of businesses that didn't talk with each other. They were silo organizations, all with their own story, even though the customers were the same. It was time to address the problem and the PLC framework proved useful once again.

Follow the Money

In the late nineties an organization was formed within Intel called PPIC (Platform Planning Integrated Communication). Their job was to fix the customer communication silos. Since all the divisions were talking with the same customers; PPIC said, "Let's have a plan to do it in a consistent manner." This meant the same story, the same manner, the same font, and so forth. The method was to get control of the distribution of the channel of information and control the product release.

Will Swope – *Director of PPIC "When PPIC was formed, the product operations believed it a waste of time. The product planners and product marketing people responsible for the launches were convinced that they were already planning at the platform level. Each operation had good relationships with the major accounts, and each operation was getting good feedback about their own products and roadmaps. The place where the system was not working, however, was in unification of message (and product timing) prior to the launch of the customers' platform. In fact, although each operation was talking to their customers, they were not talking to each other. The first time that we held a meeting of the product managers, we asked each of them to bring their customer-facing presentations to the meeting and basically give their presentation to the other operations. What we found was exactly what one would expect to find: subtle but important differences in the interpretation of the corporate "Plan of Record" (POR); Miscommunication in the presentations about the other portions of the platform, and overall, a lack of coordination on information, timing, and silicon availability that resulted in expensive implementation for the customer. None of these misses were catastrophic, but all of them resulted in less than stellar customer service.*

The first step to solve this was one customer package from all of the divisions. The integration of these update books was a pretty massive undertaking. Just getting the information in common format and timing proved to be hard, let alone assuring accuracy. The first two documents were painful to create. However, within a year all of the participants agreed that the common approach was far better internally and externally.

Another key part of alignment of the divisions was a common understanding of the markets served and a common approach to presenting the product plans to address them. We separated the analysis of the market into a separate document "Market Segment Analysis", and then tried (unsuccessfully) to divide the product plans into "what is possible" and "what is affordable." The "what is affordable" became the new Product Line Business Plans (PLBP) and the methodology of market analysis and product plans lasted a decade."

While solving this problem PPIC discovered the PLC. It was a useful tool for them to help gain consistency across different businesses (the one-to-many business leverage yet again). They worked to influence the next release of the PLC. This time they connected the PLC to strategic planning for the corporation.

Two new milestones were added in the top left-hand corner of the funnel; the Market Segment Analysis (MSA) and Business Requirements Document (BRD) hovered above and to the left of the exploration phase. The MSA represented Intel's long-range view of the market and the BRD was linked with Intel's annual product line business planning activities. The new milestones and associated documents resulted from the PPIC effort to add commonality and rigor to Intel's strategic planning process and the PLC Forum's need to connect the PLC to how Intel decides future investments. The PLC was now connected to how Intel invests its money.

The PLC was poised to deliver on its corporate-wide potential, but it lacked a corporate infrastructure necessary to scale. It was this lack of infrastructure that provided motivation for the next set of changes and would make the PLC relevant to mainstream product development. But this change in infrastructure came from an organization that approached the developers of the PLC and said the equivalent of "I am from corporate and I am here to help you." Only this time they actually meant it.

The Network

The Corporate Quality Network (CQN) was as the name describes, a network of quality organizations that spanned much of the company. In the late nineties the Intel's boards and systems quality organization was integrated into this network. In addition to product and process quality engineers, reliability engineers, regulatory experts and specialized labs, boards and systems joined and in doing so the PLC joined a corporate support organization.

Even though the PLC team was now part of CQN, ownership for this framework was new to the organization. To CQN, focused historically on traditional quality and reliability, this PLC, shown in Figure 5.1, was different and unfamiliar. Art Vargas was a longtime CQN manager and was used to working early in product definition and early development. His Design for

Quality and Reliability department was focused on defect prevention in product development. He was assigned to co-lead the inclusion of the PLC in the Network.

Art Vargas – *Design for Quality and Reliability Manager 1998 "For CQN's senior management the PLC was something they were not used to and it made them uncomfortable. They also could not see at first the potential to utilize the PLC to orient CQN activities focused on defect prevention versus defect detection and removal. For my department it made sense instantly. I had been working upstream further and further from product qualification for years, but there was nothing to orient our next steps. The PLC gave us a framework to synchronize our activities. As we integrated the PLC in CQN, we developed a corporate structure to help the further adoption of the PLC framework"*

Paul Ryan Design for Quality and Reliability – *"I was frustrated why I couldn't advance the Design for Quality and Reliability agenda. I was frustrated that I was always late. The PLC was a framework that defined when decisions get made. For people outside of the design world it was a framework to know when to intercept."*

CQN established a PLC Synergy Center, which had three responsibilities:
1. Being the definers and keepers of the corporate infrastructure
2. Being the definers and keepers of "reference" (to be explained shortly) deployment collateral
3. Being the keepers of learning and improvement loops

The PLC synergy center was expected to work with the vast army of quality and reliability engineers (QREs) deployed across the product development landscape to support, train, and consult the implementation and ultimate adoption of the PLC. In the case of adoption the literal dictionary definition of *adoption* was intended for the PLC, which meant to "take up and make one's own." This strategy stemmed from Intel's *managed autonomy* policy that was in place at the time.

Intel was exploding into many related but different products and businesses. One-size-fits-all seemed impractical and could in fact impede the growth of these new products and businesses. Within certain constraints (that would be the "managed" part) divisions were expected to act like independent companies (that would be the "autonomy" part). At its height little was off the table. Compensation plans, product ideas, and manufacturing strategies could be challenged against what was right for a particular business.

Against the backdrop of this managed autonomy environment CQN came up with this idea of three levels of PLC documentation as shown in the pyramid in Figure 5.1. The top two levels would be owned by CQN. At the highest level was a documented PLC that was part of a class of documents called *group guidelines*. A group guideline is a controlled document that:

■ Has the purpose of defining requirements to achieve synergy across operations

■ Defines a major policy with expected outcomes or principles to be followed

■ Defines high-level governing business requirements, roles, and responsibilities

■ Is no more than two pages in length

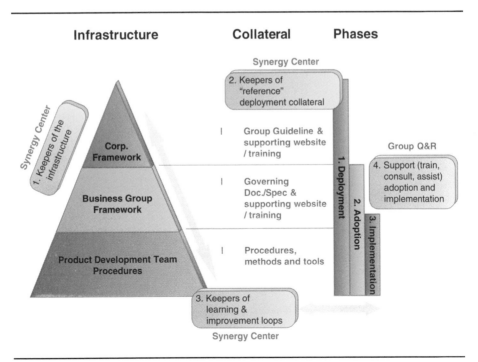

Figure 5.1   Corporate PLC Structure

The PLC Group Guideline

The synergy center took the opportunity to take the life cycle to the highest level of abstraction and blend the terms for PLC Revision 3.0 with terms commonly used in the silicon world at Intel. The PLC started in Intel's boards and systems, but it had to have a look and feel that would make it relevant to the predominant silicon development divisions of Intel. As in all things of this nature the resolution was a good compromise.

Intel Product Life Cycle

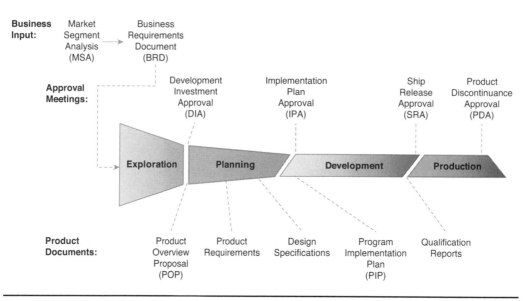

Figure 5.2   Intel Product Life Cycle
Source: Intel Product Life Cycle Group Guideline, Revision 1.0 – 1999

This high level guideline was a decent piece of process legislation that combined the accepted milestone of the emerging boards and systems PLC with the traditional documents of mainstream silicon development. For example the traditional silicon Product Implementation Plan (PIP) was coincident with the Implementation Plan Approval Meeting (IPA). Perfect. Similarly, the traditional silicon Product Overview Proposal (POP) was coincident with The Development Investment Approval Meeting (DIA). Close enough.

This was the highest level framework destined to define policy and business outcomes and achieve cross-organization synergy, but it was too general. It needed a companion document that sat between the group guideline and the very detailed procedures owned by specific work groups (see Figure 5.2). This class of document was targeted at the business unit level.

The PLC Reference Procedure

The name of the class of document is descriptive of its intent. Any business could count on the reference procedure to contain the most complete and most advanced thinking of the PLC to that point in time. CQN, the network, had intimate exposure to the entire product development landscape. They could stitch together the best practices and get concurrence from the divisions that it was the best practice embodied in a reference procedure. The businesses were free to modify for the needs of business. This was very much in line with the managed autonomy policies of the time.

Revision 4.0 of the PLC and a slightly modified 4.1, shown in Figure 5.3, was a combination of the best of Revision 3.0 with lessons learned from all business unit adoptions and was made consistent with terminology of the group guideline.

The IPLC Rev. 4.1 Reference Procedure

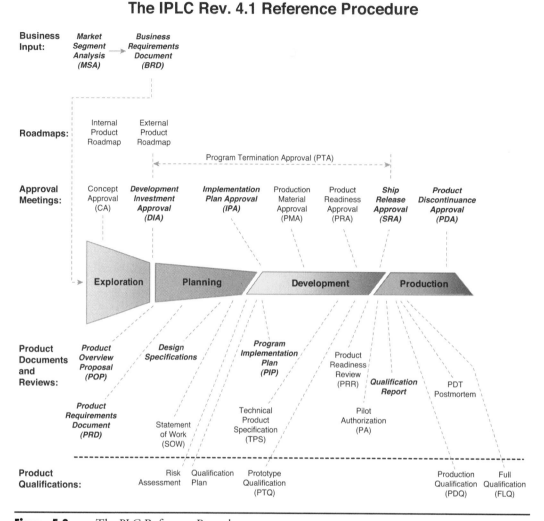

Figure 5.3 The PLC Reference Procedure
Source : Intel Product Life Cycle Reference Procedure, Revision 4.1 – 2000

The group guideline provided the synergy across the organization while the reference procedure became the new detailed baseline with the flexibility to make it work for individual businesses.

Russ Martinelli – *Server Program Manager 1999* *"When I was in the server group we combined the best of both documents. We looked at the group guideline and said 'that is not detailed enough' and then we took the reference procedure and said 'this is a little too heavy handed for us.' We then looked at both sets of milestones and determined which combination was right for the server group. We teamed up with CQN and ended up somewhere in the middle. Having two sets of guides to work off of was very valuable."*

The revision of the group guideline and the reference procedure added improved relevance to a wider audience. This revision worked for a large cross-section of the product development community. There were now enough successful adoptions that much of the skepticism was removed. Business divisions and groups heard about the success of other groups and wanted to do the same. What follows are a few of the many examples:

Desktop Chipsets used the PLC as a key tool to increase efficiency and effectiveness. They adopted their PLC focusing both on front-end planning and back-end execution. By 2002 the results yielded improvements to both Time to Money (TTM) and reaching their quality goal for product launches.

Server Motherboards adopted the PLC to drive a consistent framework and terminology between their different discrete products and functional groups. In 2001, these were in many cases different milestones and different meanings. By 2002, a common PLC across all products and functions helped reduce TTM and helped with outsourced supplier management.

Flash Memory had the PLC in place since 1998–99, although the general manager graded the effort as "necessary but insufficient." By 2000, the Flash PLC included success criteria to the end of the planning process driving ambiguity out of the expectation for the end product. Disciplined decision meetings were detailed along the lines of the framework, which got the decision making out of the hallway. Results included increased number of products qualified per year and improvements on margin per wafer start.

Input/Output (I/O) Processor implemented the PLC to set clear expectations, establish accountability, prioritize resources, and bring discipline to the early milestones of the development process. By 2001, these changed behaviors led to faster TTM in the context of increasing product complexity, zero product cancellations in development, and highly competitive product offerings.

Dialogic Corporation was acquired in 1999 and became Intel's network and communication business bringing with them a fully documented product development process that had served them well for many years. In 2001, this division decided to adopt the PLC to better integrate with other groups at Intel. They saw the PLC provide a common framework and language for product development. Product planning and decision making in this phase was a focus area along with financial tools and infrastructure to make improved qualitative and quantitative decisions. The PLC adoption provided a structured way to make commitments and an understanding of the implications of being at a certain place in the PLC.

One exception to the group guideline and reference procedure was Intel's microprocessor development divisions. They developed a life cycle that was a bit of a departure. They called it Structured Product Development, shown in Figure 5.4.

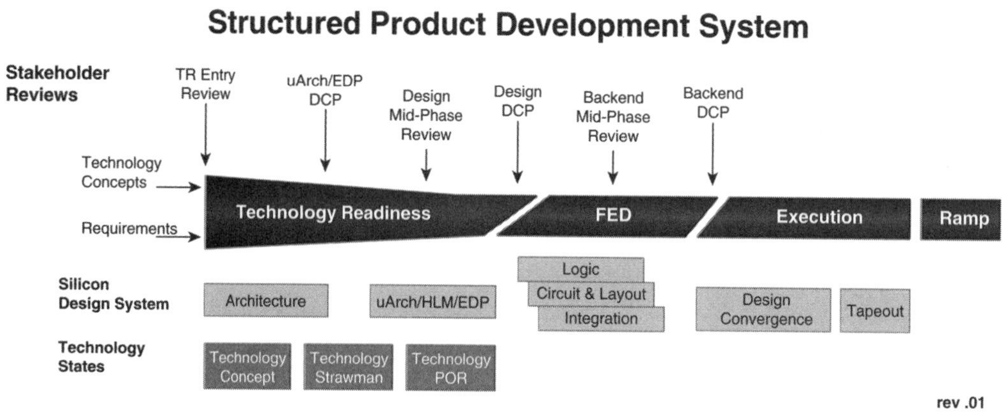

Figure 5.4   Structured Product Development System
Source: Structured Product Development System, Revision .01 – Circa 1999

The microprocessor development began developing multiple CPUs at the same time and they were doing this globally. They needed some kind of commonality to keep things straight. Senior management began driving a more structured approach to product development. It was time to become clear on phase gate criteria.

Steve Smith – VP and GM of Itanium® Processor Division 1998 "We talked about a couple of things in the Structured Product Development. One key thing was the concept of measuring complexity and understanding the products we are defining. And the other is doing the right job of selecting the features, the scope, etc. to actually manage the complexity.

We had the idea that to have a more predictable schedule and to define complexity that's allowed, you're going to manage scope and schedule in order to manage complexity through the life cycle.

We picked up some of these concepts from the silicon process development side; they had a model for process development life cycle and the amount of change that was allowed at any point in the cycle and the cost associated with the change.

The eventual outcome of this thinking is the tick-tock model that we put into place internally in 2003, and delivered products starting with Core 2 Duo in 2006, and a new product every year thereafter."

If Revision 3.0 was able to capture the early majority on the diffusion of innovation S curve, then Revisions 4.0 and 4.1 were able to capture the late majority.

"Adoption may be both an economic necessity for the late majority and the result of increasing network pressures from peers. Innovations are approached with a skeptical and cautious air, and the late majority do not adopt until most others in the system have done so. The weight of system norms must definitely favor an innovation before the late majority is convinced. The pressure of peers is necessary to motivate adoption. Their relatively scarce resources mean that most of the uncertainty about a new idea must be removed before the late majority feel that it is safe to adopt."

Everett M. Rogers – Diffusion of Innovation, Fourth Edition

Looking back at the historic PLC adoption at Intel, it isn't a pretty S curve, but it is pretty close. During this time it was a measure of how many product development organizations adopted a unique group- or division-level tailored version of a life cycle. By the end of 2002, the PLC had spread throughout most of the company (Figure 5.5).

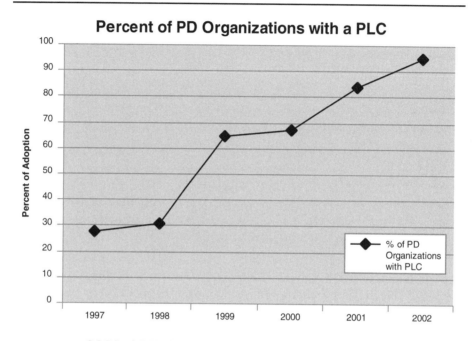

2002: 95% Adoption in Product Development

Figure 5.5   As of 2002, the Percent of Intel Organizations with a Tailored Version of the Product Life Cycle Was 95%.
Source: Maureen Reyes and Associates Inc.

So, was there attainment of the end state? Was the destination reached? Was there arrival? It could be called a milestone, but work on the PLC is never done. At this time a new set of business problems emerged that would cause the many divisions at Intel to look at how they adopted life cycles. This time they would have to look at the life cycle from a platform perspective. This meant connecting PLCs across business silos would be important. The independence of managed autonomy was coming to an end. The businesses would have to adapt and so would the PLC.

But first a short break to reflect on lessons learned from the development and adoption of the PLC in this timeframe.

Lessons Learned

- In order to scale across the corporation, the PLC needs an infrastructure.
- The PLC had to connect programs to the money decisions and strategic goals.

Questions

1. How can you link product and financial decisions across the life cycle?
2. Do you see year-over-year improvement in adoption, business results, or other measures of success?

Chapter **6**

Intermission

It is striking how history, when resting on the memory of men, always touches the bounds of mythology.

— Leopold von Ranke

At this point it is useful to take a step back and review some central themes learned from past events that guided and continues to guide the evolution of the PLC in product development and in areas adjacent to product development. The objective is to observe basic elements of change agency that lead to the adoption of the PLC across a significant percentage of organizations at Intel.

Retrospective

A midpoint retrospective, or critical look at the past, can reveal lessons to date, good and bad. These lessons provide course correction on the current project going forward, and can inform follow-on projects that haven't reached this point in their definition and development. Retrospectives are a better memory system when done periodically across time, rather than waiting until the end when people have left the project or are thinking about the next project assignment. This chapter is a retrospective on key lessons in the first half of the book. Were they one-time occurrences? Or do they prove true repeatedly?

It was the use of a painful disconfirming event to properly frame a problem, to define corrective action, which lead to a potential solution. As we have seen, the solution was not always successful, but there has to be an emotionally charged reason for people to change.

When the right solution was in place, business results followed. To aggregate the business results from the first half of the book, they generally fell into the following categories:

- More effective communication
- Clearer expectations and decision making
- Disciplined and synchronized execution
- Better examination of a business problem
- The combination of the above leading to better time to market

Below are a few examples to illustrate this.

Brian Walker – Server Chipsets Operations Manager 2002 *"Our problem was classic: missed deadlines. We were looking for a standard, disciplined approach to be more predictable in delivering products. At the time the different teams would do their program reviews with the general manager and they would come in with different milestones. It was difficult for the GM to get his finger on the pulse of 'are you on track or not?'*

Each team wanted to do it differently. There were challenges in terms of the front end of design aligning pre–tape out activities to validation and back end aligning post–tape out activities across debug, validation, and manufacturing. We were trying to sync up logic and circuit design. We were trying to knit it all together, but we had many issues with communication.

But over the years we developed and deployed our PLC and it was highly successful. We still use it today and we still refine it as we are using it. And we very much value the milestones we put in place. Our GM understands what they are so when we do execution reviews we still line up those milestones. It's been very successful for our group."

The PLC often starts with the basics such as common milestones with agreed-upon exit criteria and enough discipline to meet the intent of the exit criteria. As we saw in the early chapters, when you put the basics in place you can then spend your energy fixing more advanced problems. In the boards and systems example, after fixing the engineering to manufacturing handoff issues, more focus was applied upstream in validation, design, and requirements definition. You put those basics in place and you have the foundation for better discussions. These would often be better business discussions, decisions, and results.

Russ Martinelli – *"What I really liked was I was in partnership with my business unit manager for the first time. What the PLC did for that experience is that it gave us a common set of things to talk about from different perspectives. I was obviously worried about execution; getting through exploration, planning, and development. I was responsible for the deliverables in each key phase and milestone, but the business unit manager also used those very same milestones to make business decisions. So we had conversations about business and execution and how the two things were tied together. The PLC served as a framework for collaboration between me, the program manager, and the business unit manager."*

The Definition of a Standard

How standard should a PLC be and how do you measure conformance to the PLC? At Intel the answer has shifted over time. During the age of managed autonomy it was expected that organizations would take the reference procedure and modify it to suit the needs of their business. As we will see in the second half of this book, when the need for consistent communication across organizations becomes important the need for a more common life cycle becomes the expectation. The important point is that the answer to "how common?" is up to the businesses as they address their competitive and economic environment.

Brian Bingold – Director, Corporate Platform Office 2009 *"In the earlier parts of my career where we used the life cycle, I know within the confines of a certain business unit the usage of the framework was pretty consistent. Working across business groups I think Intel culture plays a role in allowing businesses to tailor it to the business needs so what we would see is commonality of vocabulary where you needed to work across businesses and tailoring to the specific needs of their business. This works as long as you can come back to a common gold version and capture the lessons over time."*

The PLC is a balancing act between the opposite poles of anarchy and rigid command and control. Oddly, when groups adopt a PLC there is less tendency to return to anarchy as there is to turn it into a religion. Compare something like the U.S. Constitution to a PLC religion. The Constitution is a set of enduring principles that fit on a few pages crafted by mortal men and that can be amended over time. When the PLC becomes a religion it is defined by a higher authority so it must be followed without question. Conformance leaves you vaguely hopeful for product development heaven whereas the opposite would mean product development hell.

Sticking with the religious analogy, there is this notion of a "Moses Complex." In the Bible, Moses sees a burning bush, ascends Mount Sinai, and comes back with stone tablets. The tablets endowed the holder with unique knowledge, which could be shared as commandments with the less enlightened. It is interesting that in the creation of the PLC; some people actually believed they had the same unique knowledge experience. Be wary of a process person who says the equivalent of: "I had this great meeting with God today and we know what is best for you."

The Moses Complex comes with two problematic behaviors. First, the view is one based on Utopia rather than being grounded in the pragmatic possibilities given the maturity of the organization. The second is the process just became more important than the business results it is trying to affect. The Moses Complex is not just exhibited in things like life cycles. Look at any good idea like CMM, Lean, or Six Sigma where the enlightened ones have driven the concepts to an onerous, impractical extreme.

Consider the following:

"The thought of standards makes a lot of people cringe. That is because they confuse standardization with uniformity. They think standards somehow discourage creativity. They perceive standards as a control mechanism to prevent individuals from performing the job in the manner they view as best. They view standards as restrictive and rigid, even oppressive.

Developed and used properly, a standard is none of those things. The skepticism and cynicism stems from the fact that in most organizations standards are all those evil things. Most companies use central committees to develop standards. They use the words 'standard' and 'edict' interchangeably. The standard is, in effect, permanent. Big mistake.

A true standard is the exact opposite. The difference at companies like Toyota that believe in the kaizen way is this:

- *Standards are created by the individuals performing the work*

- *Standards are dynamic, and not everything gets standardized*

A standard is simply an established best-known method or practice followed until a better way is discovered, tested and accepted. A standard lets you know where there's problem. It shows you where to begin the search for solutions. It prevents mistakes from being made twice. It lets you capture and retain knowledge and expertise. And it helps you stay safe." Matthew E. May – The Elegant Solution, Toyota's Formula for Mastering Innovation

Tom Rampone – *"So the PLC in any point in time represents our best understanding of what we can do today, or yesterday by the time we are implementing it again. I think it's important we are always looking for ways to do better in this instantiation than we did the last time we were able to write things down. So to me pushing the envelope on the PLC is about a serious focus on continuous improvement and getting better generation to generation. It's about making risk and judgment decisions about whether you are ready to proceed in your mind. If you are following all the milestones and all the exit criteria, you probably are not pushing it.*

Process is a means to an end; not the goal in itself. Command and control people don't like this because they don't trust others to get it right. Milestones need to have teeth, but you should focus on intent, not overly on conformance."

Using the PLC

With a properly balanced and continuously improving life cycle, program managers and business leaders can utilize the framework to drive results. However, with the flexible life cycle comes the responsibility to influence and lead.

Russ Martinelli – *"I came to Intel from aerospace. When I first saw the PLC it was a sigh of relief because what I didn't see was heavy-handed military specifications with all these 'thou shalt do this.' It actually gave me the freedom to act within these big business milestones and it allowed me to lead my team with a more freedom. However it was a little disconcerting for me at the same time because it wasn't prescriptive, which was what I was used to in aerospace. Now I had to learn other skills on the leadership side as opposed to the management side where you just had to manage to specs. To drive a product through the PLC requires leadership.*

For a program manager the thing I like about the life cycle is that it puts tension in the system which allows you to motivate your team. When you have a milestone or gate coming up, you can use that to your advantage as a motivator, and a focusing point, to create a sense of urgency based on time to market goals. Just a checklist would not do it for me, but certainly a review with a general manager or vice president with the functional managers would. Especially if I got the functional managers to come to that meeting with me and explain where we were."

Functional organizations discovered that they could use the PLC to orient their work and show how they added value to development of the product. An added benefit is gathering and feeding back of crucial data from the right side (execution) of the funnel to the left side (planning) where the feedback can prevent rework or waste at the far right end on the product and with the customer.

An example of using the framework for a functional organization is Intel customer support. Working with the PLC team they defined an *overlay*, as shown in Figure 6.1. Conceptually an overlay is like a PLC tailored for a specific organization, only this is for a specific function at Intel like customer support. The function-specific milestones are overlaid on a released life cycle highlighting key events where the functional organization either gets information to do their work or provides information back to the product development organizations.

Jeff Marchek – Customer Support Manager 2007 *"Back when I was a product support engineer, it was my job to 'engineer' support services for products. Intel at the time didn't consider support services as part of the product. So we needed to up our influence in what those product groups were doing and integrate ourselves in those groups to realize that goal. We saw the original PLC and most of the documentation was focused on marketing and engineering and their roles. We needed an overlay to show where support engineering comes in, plays a role, and how we add value.*

The overlay really worked for us. We still use it today. It is still standard language in our organization for all our support engineers. When a new support engineer is hired, that is one of the first things to teach and indoctrinate them with. I am a program manager now and we are moving up the food chain. It's becoming even a bigger deal now with platform product and services bundled direct to consumer products."

Service & Support Life Cycle
(Released 5-22-2007)

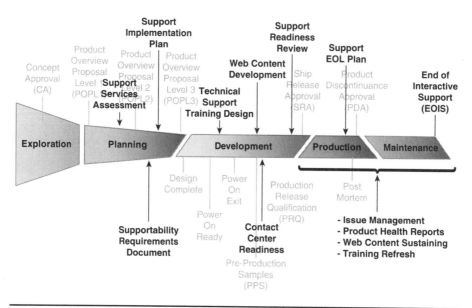

Figure 6.1   Service and Support Life Cycle
Source: Service and Support Life Cycle – 2007

The overlay concept enables a function or business group to define how they manage their work relative to the product development community. Other functional overlays include: security, product regulatory and specific business-division and group-level implementations.

Not all the adaptations of a life cycle in the corporation are reflected in an overlay. Many internal organizations outside of product development take the life cycle concepts and customize the framework to fit their needs; they define, manage, and deliver their "products" using a very specific life cycle. Examples exist in Manufacturing, Human Resources, Intel Press, and User-Centered Design.

Below is an example from Intel's e-Business group (Figure 6.2), which eventually merged with Information Technology.

Dennis Skinner – eBusiness Program Manager 2001 *"Our PLC experience was shortly after the e-Business group was formed. The company wanted to bring together the many component organizations that were dabbling in e-commerce at the time to increase economy of scale and innovative thought. As we formed as a group, problems with decision making and program/project management were huge sources of frustration. We found a lot of problems people were talking about had at their root a lack of a structure, a skeleton. A framework was needed for managing projects that made sure all the right things happened at appropriate times. We found the PLC in the spring of 2001 and by the summer we were implementing the PLC on prototype products. By the end of the year we launched broad deployment. When we merged with IT the rest of the organization adopted PLC. It has been modified maybe 10 or 20 percent, but a decade later it is still being used by a vast majority of IT projects.*

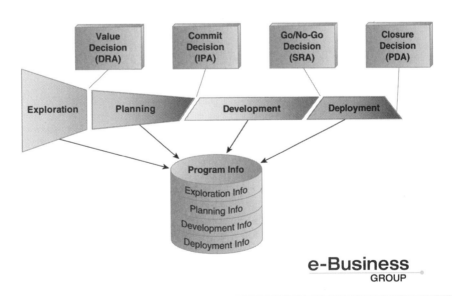

Figure 6.2   eBG Program Life Cycle *Source: eBG Program Lifecycle – 2001*

Even as the Product Life Cycle was being used and modified across the company, another need was evolving. Platform management and development had unique requirements that necessitated a different view of the life cycle framework. There was yet another problem to solve.

Lessons Learned

- The PLC is a balancing act between the opposite poles of anarchy and rigid command and control.
- The flexible nature of a life cycle requires leadership to drive products through the lifecycle and the purpose is business results.

Questions

1. Will you need multiple levels of definition? Will you define a high level corporate framework and then a reference procedure or procedures?

2. Is your organization ready and willing to capture and communicate lessons, successes, and mistakes?

3. How will you measure success? Success year to year and by individual initiatives.

4. Is your improvement work tied to the success of the corporation?

Chapter 7

The Platform

Your most unhappy customers are your greatest source of learning.
— Bill Gates

From 1999 through 2003 three product development groups, Mobile, Servers, and Desktop, began to independently view their work from a platform perspective. Thinking about platforms was not completely new at Intel. The company had to think of elements of a platform when it was delivering kits of components early on. This was improved from 1988 to 1999 when notebooks, optimized for power, needed the chipset and processor to be integrated and co-validated. However from 1999 to 2003 the problem became acute in these three groups. Each started with a business problem they were trying to solve. Mobile was developing the brand Centrino® and while they did not have a documented platform version of a PLC, they had to think from the platform perspective nonetheless. The Servers group was thinking about systems that had a wide range of options such as operating systems and memory configurations. They did develop a platform view of the PLC. The Desktop group was thinking about complexity. Intel needed to validate products together and coordinate the launch dates of the products that needed to fit together. Intel's mobile, server, and desktop businesses needed to think and develop products from the platform perspective; but at this point there was no common understanding of what the platform was.

Justin Rattner – *"When you think of platforms and how they relate to the PLC, you have to think of a stack of PLCs. Each of the individual ingredients has its own life cycle it follows and now those life cycles have to be integrated across product and organizational boundaries to deliver a more complete solution to our customer's customer."*

Desktop—Managing Across the Silos

The Desktop group at the time defined the *platform* as "a set of interdependent ingredients associated with a unique processor, chipset, or a processor chipset combination, all qualified to launch as the same time." A *platform ingredient* was defined as a "component of the platform required to be available at launch; that may or may not be manufactured by Intel." Intel's customers need all the ingredients done at the same time to start the final validation process that certifies the computer product in its final configuration.

In 1999 senior management within the Desktop business pulled Ralph Brooks and Bill McAuliffe into new positions to fix the problem of synchronizing all the elements of a platform so that they could integrate more easily by their immediate customer. In 2000 the Desktop business created a Platform Management group. Now Ralph and Bill had a new job and a problem to solve: Define, manage, and execute the desktop platform programs acceptable from the customer's perspective.

Bill McAuliffe – Platform Program Manager 2001 *"They put platform responsibility under the desktop division while the CPU and chipset development was in other divisions. So there wasn't a cohesive schedule integration of the entire platform other than the end launch date. The intermediate checkpoints that are so critical for an integrated design were not connected and so nobody understood the risk level or readiness until near the end when panic set in. Sometimes it's simple things that bring communication and understanding between teams. Ralph and I started a risk assessment tool that was simply a graphic where you set a needle on a range from red (showstopper risk) to green (little to no risk). That became the Health-o-Meter and started showing up in reviews. Now teams depending on others for an intermediate deliverable could understand their exposure. It also became the catalyst for more detailed discussions between teams ahead of something being obviously broken. So Ralph and I worked with several key people with expertise in process development to turn new system into a scalable model. It took the next year to enroll the different organizations. We made our first platform management proposal in 2000. We each took a project and there was enough success that in 2001, Ralph and I each hired two people to expand from the pilot. From there it accelerated into a new way of doing things."*

Ralph Brooks – Platform Program Manager 2001 *"We defined new roles and responsibilities, tools processes, et cetera. We defined platform program manager roles, platform development management systems, joint platform teams (JPT), at the JPT forum. The time we spent getting the enrollment of senior management paid off in supporting these new roles. However, when we expanded from our successful pilot programs we needed a system to manage all this. How do you create a system that enables you to take the various ingredients and make the sum of the ingredients greater than the individual parts?"*

From a discrete product perspective, the Desktop group was one of the birthplaces of the PLC. It seemed fitting that this group would be one of the early developers of the platform life cycle. Sarah Nesland was now integrated into the Desktop group. She made a proposal to Bill McAuliffe for a platform view of the PLC. From that initial proposal she then talked to both Bill and Ralph. Together they sketched out the whole concept of a platform PLC and named it the Platform Development Management System, shown in Figure 7.1. They wanted to try it out and worked with the program management support team to help and away they went.

Sarah Nesland – Platform Process Manager 2001 *"Laurie LeChevalier-Litvin and I worked together to figure out what the whole scheduling system would be like because we wanted to manage at the synchronization points, not the low, low level details. Otherwise we would have been overwhelmed with complexity because there are just too many ingredients. So the notion around the platform PLC was one of those glimmers of intuition of where the PLC needed to go next. Bill and Ralph had a gap from a program management standpoint. Ralph had a spreadsheet, but there wasn't anything to enable them to repeatedly launch a platform. It did not seem to me that much of an abstraction that a variant of the PLC could be applied to the platform. You could manage at that higher level and manage those higher level goals.*

Developing a system became a matter of survival. The major elements of this Platform Development Management System included

- *Decision-making framework to include what decisions are made in what venues and by what people*

- *Automated scheduling tool and schedule update process*

- *Platform requirements, success criteria, and indicators"*

Laurie LeChevalier-Litvin – Program Analyst 2001 *"We didn't start from scratch. There were PLCs all over the company, but nothing documented at the platform level. There were many ways to look at the PLC and they all affected the platform. When we did put a platform view on the PLC and created a platform management system it drove commonality even across the ingredient PLCs. It drove consistent language, formed meetings that didn't exist before, and helped communication across boundaries. It broke down the silos."*

The decision-making framework was in fact the platform view of the PLC. The key ingredients were identified and their appropriate PLC milestones were synced up with the platform milestones. This was applied to a platform/ingredient intercept.

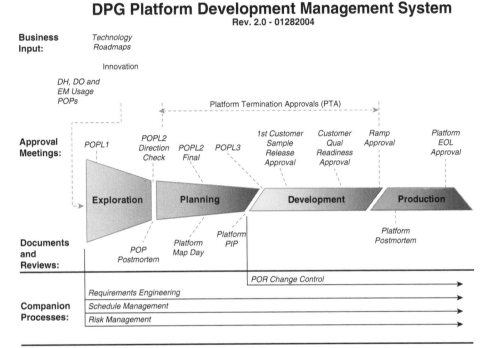

Figure 7.1   Desktop Products Group: Platform Development Management System, circa 2004

The scheduling tool and process was started with the first-ever platform map day for the same platform/ingredient intercept. This activity ensured all ingredient schedules were synchronized and dependencies understood. The results were loaded into a Microsoft Project[†]–based scheduling tool with defined expectations on how the tool would be updated and how the Joint Platform Teams would manage progress and disconnects. Lastly platform requirements, success criteria, and indicators were developed. A minimum set was defined that grew over time to be much more comprehensive. Results were demonstrated on the first pilot intercept.

Sarah Nesland – *"The pilot...demonstrated business results in three ways:*

- *Early revenue for the chipset and three additional design wins*

- *Increased efficiency for platform program managers*

- *The synchronization of ingredient owners and functional group*

During the program an opportunity presented itself to pull in the schedule of the chipset. The platform team needed to understand if all the ingredients could be synced up with a pull-in of the chipset. Because of the system in place they were able to quickly assess all the impacts and the associated risks. Armed with this information, each group took action that resulted in successfully modifying their ingredient level Plan of Record (POR) and thus were able to pull in the platform schedule by a full month."

The pilot intercept was successful enough that senior management took notice and Ralph Brooks committed to using the Platform Development Management System for all desktop programs going forward. After about a year of honing the platform life cycle, platform map days, integrated schedules, and risk, it was time for the desktop group to look further upstream in the life cycle and focus on the platform requirements.

A Change in Perspective

It did not take very long focusing on platform requirements to realize when you focus on the platform you are not just focusing on the requirements of the direct customer, the original equipment manufacturer (OEM). You have to focus on the end-user needs and usage models. You needed to focus on solution requirements of your intended platform.

This change in perspective was already taking shape in the mobile Centrino® experience. Engineers came to work worrying about four things: performance (the best notebook), small form factor (not too heavy), battery life, and Wi-Fi† communications. These were all end-user pain points.

The focus on the end user and usage models had already started at Intel. For example, Genevieve Bell joined Intel in 1998 as a researcher in Corporate Technology Group's People and Practices Research team—Intel's first social science–oriented research team. Her background was studying the intersection of technology and society. Eric Dishman helped launch Intel's Digital Health Group in 1999. He founded the Product Research and Innovation team responsible for driving Intel's worldwide healthcare research, new product innovation, strategic planning, and health policy and standards activities. All targeted end user needs.

User-Centered Design (UCD) was an organization in place whose organizational name was also its best practice. User-Centered Design is a modern, widely practiced design philosophy rooted in the idea that users must take center stage in the design of any computer system. It is a process of product development that starts with end users and their needs rather than with technology. In UCD, tasks were performed by human factors engineers.

The desktop focus on platform requirements and usage started on the platform intercept scheduled for launch in 2005. They took their lead from the Centrino experience and usage model and use case work already in flight. Thought leaders who had experience with both requirements and usage developed training to make sure terms and concepts were defined and consistent with industry. They worked with the planning teams to translate the concepts to practical application on specific platform intercepts. Consider the following in Erik Simmons' presentation, which discusses usage as one of the three tacit platform categories.

"Platforms are usually complete enough to support discussions on platforms usage and user experience. Intel's definition of platform includes a bullet focused on delivering new usage models. Many of the functions and properties of a platform that matter most to consumers are emergent; that is, they are not present in any single ingredient—only in the complete platform. Emergent platform behaviors are where much of the user experience is created.

Intel's core platform business strategy is the building block model. Since Intel relies on partners to create complete solutions, it cannot control those solutions as it might in the Full Platform model. But, It would be risky to simply concede platform usage characteristics to partners, since their failure would quickly become Intel's failure. It is possible to guide and influence complete solution creation while remaining in the building block economic model.

Platform-based validation should be driven by technical specification and end user experience. In a competitive marketplace, user experience can be a purchase driver and brand loyalty creator. While it is impractical to validate every complete solution produced using Intel platforms, Intel can demonstrate that it is feasible to meet user experience requirements while also meeting business and technology requirements. Meeting a technical specification is of little use if that specification doesn't yield an acceptable user experience."

– Erik Simmons, "Three Facets of Platforms and Platform Transformation."

The first attempt had no overarching requirements or actionable use cases. The second had actionable use cases, but they were not properly integrated into the life cycle and grew stale and had to be rewritten in a reactive, ad hoc manner. As the program teams gained experience from previous attempts, use cases were written at the appropriate time in the life cycle and the validation team was able to use them effectively. The focus on associating requirements and usage at the appropriate times in the platform life cycle prompted continued evolution in thought as to the other capabilities that needed to be evolved and synchronized with the life cycle.

The Platform Execution Model

During 2002 and 2003 the CQN Life Cycle Team developed a representation of the life cycle and it supporting capabilities. Through discussion there came this notion that the life cycle as a framework was necessary, but not sufficient. You need capabilities to hang off this framework to enable product development to be more predictable and repeatable. The Platform Execution Model was developed to represent this objective, as illustrated in Figure 7.2.

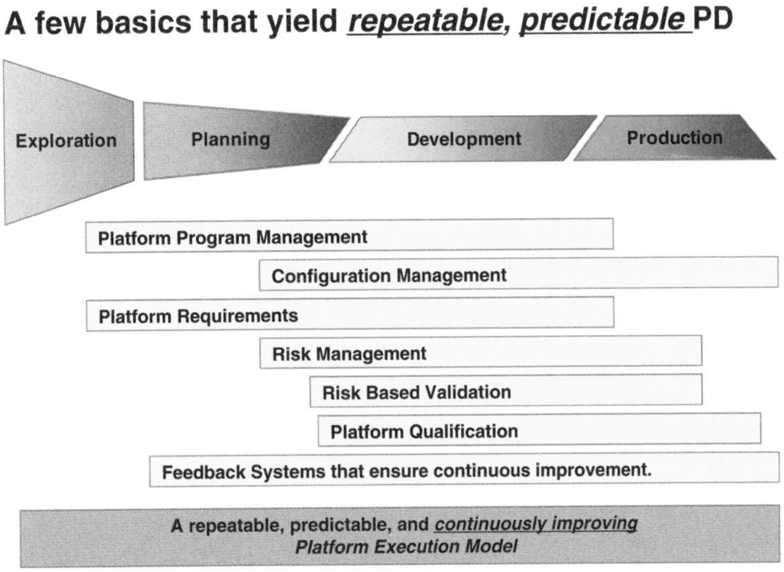

A few basics that yield _repeatable, predictable_ PD

Exploration   Planning   Development   Production

Platform Program Management

Configuration Management

Platform Requirements

Risk Management

Risk Based Validation

Platform Qualification

Feedback Systems that ensure continuous improvement.

A repeatable, predictable, and _continuously improving_
Platform Execution Model

Figure 7.2   The Platform Execution Model – 2003

The Platform Execution Model represented the next incremental maturing in thinking and a more holistic view of what it would take to bring a baseline of predictability and repeatability to product development. The various capabilities reflected the current and projected work of many product development organizations and the organizations that supported product development.

There were blueprints to work from. The Capability Maturity Model (CMM) available at the time called out those capabilities that needed to be in place to achieve repeatability as shown in Figure 7.3.

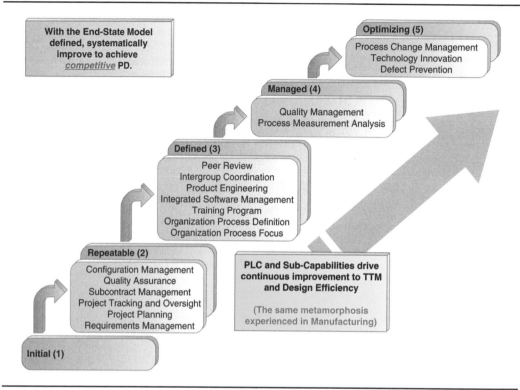

With the End-State Model defined, systematically improve to achieve _competitive_ PD.

Optimizing (5)
Process Change Management
Technology Innovation
Defect Prevention

Managed (4)
Quality Management
Process Measurement Analysis

Defined (3)
Peer Review
Intergroup Coordination
Product Engineering
Integrated Software Management
Training Program
Organization Process Definition
Organization Process Focus

Repeatable (2)
Configuration Management
Quality Assurance
Subcontract Management
Project Tracking and Oversight
Project Planning
Requirements Management

PLC and Sub-Capabilities drive continuous improvement to TTM and Design Efficiency

(The same metamorphosis experienced in Manufacturing)

Initial (1)

Figure 7.3 Capability Maturity Model *Source: Adapted from the Capability Maturity Model for the Platform Execution Model – 2003*

The first CMM was a result of a program between the US Department of Defense (DoD) and Carnegie Mellon's Software Engineering Institute to improve the quality and consistency of software engineering. This program was created in response to an unacceptable amount of missed delivery dates on software projects for the DoD. The first CMM was published for software in 1991. Benefits were realized and other disciplines started to apply the CMM principles in such areas as systems engineering and integrated product and process development. The Platform Execution Model uses capabilities consistent with CMM level 2, nudging its way to level 3. It was the goal to shoot for. It was also during this time that the Platform Life Cycle in the Servers group fully took shape.

The Server Platform Program Life Cycle

In 1998 Diane Bryant came from the Mobile Products Group as Director of Engineering to help fix the server microprocessor. By 2001 her boss who ran the Server group was on a bent to have servers *"think systems."* In short, think platforms from a server perspective.

Diane Bryant – *"The complexity of servers with the multiple operating systems, memory and I/O configurations, and varying workloads compelled the server organization to be the first to think and operate at a solutions level. This required a significant shift from Intel's historical silicon-centric view. I was given the charter to "make it happen" for servers, which started with building a small and senior Platform Program Manager team.*

Ralph Brooks – *"The server organization came in a little later and we shared with Diane and her staff the structure and tools that we had created and they liked it so much they took it and ran with it. They took it further than we had. They had more resources, they had more desire, or maybe it was because they were doing a full platform already inherent in delivering a server as opposed to a motherboard. One thing the server group did really well was documentation and a Web site. That was to a large degree their influencing point and selling point."*

Diane's team defined new Platform Teams called Platform Execution Teams, PXTs, as opposed to Joint Product Teams, JPTs. They created new forums for engagement and decision making. They took a look at the desktop view of a platform life cycle and made it better by documenting the life cycle and making it widely accessible via a formal Web site. The new view was labeled the EPG Platform PLC and was in use by 2003, as shown in Figure 7.4.

Bruce Wollstein – Server Platform Program Manager 2003 *"Let's talk specifically about the Platform PLC. I think establishing how you manage platform execution is a very fundamental thing you have to start with and you need to show that it is different from the ingredient level PLC. The "aha" is this isn't an ingredient-based discussion any more—this is a platform-based discussion. To start that discussion you have to understand and grow your definition of what a platform really means. That discussion has evolved over time and driven our development models over time. You start wrapping more and more platform features around the ingredients and now we are talking about something a little bit more complex. You start getting people out of their silos. That is what made us look at things differently over time."*

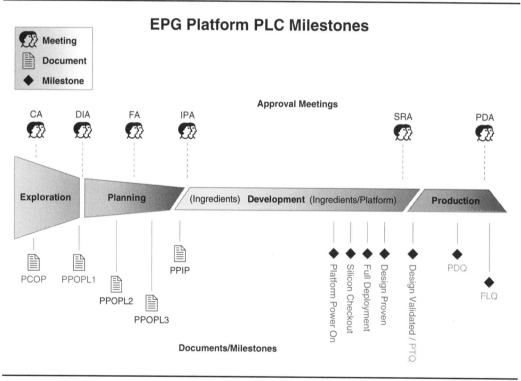

Figure 7.4   Server Platform Life Cycle, Circa 2003

Centrino launched in 2003 and was a big success. In the Strategic Long Range Planning (SLRP) session early in 2004 Paul Otellini expressed his frustration that more groups at Intel were not taking this platform perspective. The new perspective expanded from the pure silicon speeds and feeds perspective to that of providing solutions to end users.

Someone in the audience observed that Diane Bryant had already figured out how to plan and execute from a platform perspective. Diane was assigned as the initiative owner and was authorized to recruit people from across Intel's product development, quality, and human resources groups to participate in definition of the strategies, goals, and plans to transform Intel into a platform company.

Lessons Learned

■ The need to manage complexity drove platform thinking.

■ Another driver in the shift to a platform life cycle was the business need for user-focused solutions.

■ Life cycles are necessary but not sufficient; the capabilities that "align" to the framework are crucial in effective results.

Questions

1. What in your business equates with the need to manage complexity?

2. Are the product development capabilities tied to the decision-making framework?

Chapter 8

Platform Transformation

All models are wrong, but some models are useful.

—George Box

One of the outcomes from SLRP 2004 was a direction from Craig Barrett on platform management: "Ensure accurate and timely planning, decision-making, and coordination across groups for all platform solutions." In the third quarter of 2004, Diane Bryant was appointed the Director of the Corporate Platform Office (CPO) with the charter to drive the transformation of the corporation from a component-optimized company to a platform-optimized company. By the fourth quarter of 2004 Diane was driving a robust platform agenda across the company under the sponsorship of Paul Otellini.

The Corporate Platform Office

Platform transformation was initiated in part by the commoditization of the personal computer. By 2004 the end users perceived little difference among CPU speeds, which was the PC industry's primary marketing paradigm until 2004. At the same time, the OEMs were hollowing out as they were responding to margin pressure and staffing down. Original design manufacturers (ODMs) at the time were offering higher levels of design and architecture and were therefore gaining influence over design/architecture choices. These industry conditions and trends influenced Intel's shift to the platform.

Intel recognized growth opportunities for emerging and existing markets through a shift to a platform strategy. There was a need to increase revenue and margin. There was a need to grow the total available market (TAM). Different from Intel's traditional technology push, there was a growing sense of importance to develop technology focused on end-user needs and requirements. This would be part of Intel thinking and acting like a platform company. The company realized a platform transformation strategy was required for Intel to remain competitive and relevant in the computing industry.

Diane Bryant – Director Corporate Platform Office 2004 *"Intel's platform transformation ushered in Intel 3.0. Intel 1.0 was the memory company, Intel 2.0 was the microprocessor company, and Intel 3.0 was to be the platform company. The Corporate Platform Office (CPO) agenda came together fairly quickly in the back half of 2004. We provided a common definition of a platform for the company. We established the tenets of platform success. We defined the core elements of a company-wide platform system. One of the elements of this system was a platform-level life cycle, standardized across the company."*

This strategy had many focus areas and tenets for platform success. Besides the formation of the Corporate Platform Office, there were substantial changes to product development organizations changing them to platform groups where the organizational focus was on developing complete technology platforms. There was increased investment in usage models and use case development that came with the realization that user value was important for Intel's success in the market. Intel's shift to platforms drove the need for new leadership roles in areas such as platform program management, marketing, strategic planning, and architecture. There were changes to the decision-making framework and practices. There were new metrics and an employee bonus goal related to specific platform transformation objectives.

Corporate Platform Definition:

Intel defines a platform as an integrated set of ingredients that enables targeted usage models, grows existing markets, and creates new markets, and which delivers greater end-user benefits than the sum of its parts.

Tenets of Platform Success:

Define

End User/Market Driven: Align technologies, hardware, software, ecosystem, and the brand with end user requirements, usage models, and a clear value proposition

Develop

Intel and Ecosystem-Aligned Execution: Align Intel and external ingredient execution and maximize Intel revenue and strategic value

Deliver

Industry Leadership: Deliver a compelling platform solution at launch integrated with a marketing program to drive demand and value

One of these objectives was definition of a development system optimized for the platform. Many of Intel's thought leaders got together to agree on the "as-is" system optimized for the ingredients and define the "should-be" optimized for the platform.

The Platform Summit

In October of 2004 these product development thought leaders from architecture, planning, technologists, marketing, finance, program management, and human resources gathered to define the platform-optimized system. Preparation over a number of weeks mapped the existing system as a baseline. The objective of the new system was first and foremost to deliver platform success.

Steve Smith – *"At that meeting were thought leaders who had been thinking about platforms in their own business units for years. Now it was time to come together to put cross business capabilities and practices into place to accelerate Intel's platform transformation."*

This would be done in part by addressing platform complexities and interdependencies. The scope would be both internal to Intel and external to the ecosystem and would be inclusive of processes, methodologies, and tools. Across a yet-to-be-defined company-wide platform life cycle, the system would be inclusive of the end user, technology exploration, platform planning, platform development/execution, and platform launch. More specifically at the summit this cross-section of thought leaders were assigned to the following teams that in total would define the platform system:

- Technology processes defined and deployed in support of the platform and in use by the businesses.
- Common scheduling methodology ratified with training underway for both ingredient and platform businesses.
- Common demand and build plan methodologies deployed across ingredient and platform businesses and production.
- Common risk management methodology deployed across the ingredient and platform businesses.
- Cross-group platform zero-based budget (ZBB) process deployed.
- Common platform life cycle defined to include common processes, milestones, and quality criteria, and deployed across the platform businesses.

Platform summit task teams were commissioned to include one task team chartered with defining a program life cycle that would be common between groups, focused on end-user platform requirements that would synchronize the platform ingredients and ecosystem. It was a big bandwagon and many people jumped on.

The Platform Program Life Cycle (PPLC)

Sub-teams were created to examine the exploration, planning, and development phase of the platform program life cycle concurrently. The sub-teams not only included planners and platform program managers from the server, desktop, and mobile groups, but also representatives from marketing, ecosystem enabling, validation, CQN, and manufacturing. This was a big corporate party and nobody wanted to miss getting their special interests into this swelling piece of corporate legislation.

The three sub-teams ran concurrently, each agreeing first to common milestones and synchronization points (see Figure 8.1). New milestones that had never been defined before were conceptualized and written down.

In the development phase, defining platform qualification was the primary objective. The milestone name was Platform Qualified (PLQ) and it had never been identified before. The intended purpose of this milestone was to ensure the platform meet the customer and end user expectations in time for launch. The PLQ criteria were:

■ Platform and ingredient requirements must match

■ Ingredient development milestones must align in time to support platform critical path

■ Platform must demonstrate acceptability as defined by the platform requirements

■ Launch-required ecosystem core set in ingredients must be ready

■ Post-launch support plan must be enacted

A secondary objective in the development phase was early detection and correction of problems through status against PLQ objectives. In this regard all the rest of the development milestones were called milestones, but they were really synchronization points to see if you were on track for the qualification milestone. They were in fact risk-reduction synchronization points.

In the planning phase, the primary objective was tackling the vexing platform chicken-and-egg problem. If the development system is optimized for the platform, then logically the platform would be the first mover in defining platform requirements at the beginning of the planning phase to guide the requirements of the ingredients. Conversely, the ingredients would wrap up their plan of record (POR) at the planning phase ahead of the platform wrapping up its POR at the end of the planning phase. The two problems with this logical approach were:

1. Microprocessor planning starts five years before the platform launch and nobody could figure out how to plan a platform that far in advance.

2. Some of the ingredients don't even start planning until the platform is well into development.

PPLC Linkage to Ingredients

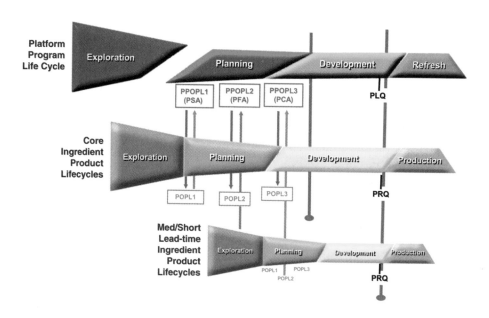

Figure 8.1 The Relationship of the New Platform Program Life Cycle to Multiple Ingredient Product Life Cycles. *Source: Intel Platform Program and Product Life Cycle Specification – 2006*

The secondary objective was to better organize the buckets of work in the planning phase and make this consistent across silo'd planning teams that each had their own planning approach. By the end of 2005 the planning teams had an agreement in principle as to the major approval meetings in the planning phase. These were to be tested on specific product intercepts in 2006. From the beginning of the planning phase to the end these were the conceptually agreed to approval meetings. Again sequentially spaced in time they were as follows:

- Platform Scope Approval: The Platform Scope Approval meeting identifies market usage and technology requirements. The content should include business requirements, usage requirements, technologies, ecosystem, and a plan to get to the next approval meeting.

- Platform Feasibility Approval: Identify usage model and technology targets for the platform. The content is the same as the above with the addition of platform requirements, risk mitigation, software, validation, quality and reliability, manufacturing, and marketing considerations.

- Platform Commit Approval: Platform Plan of Record (POR) closure and grading against market requirements. The content is the same as Feasibility Approval only these are committed by the groups who will execute.

In the *Exploration Phase* nobody knew what to do, but people tried. It was some good thinking, but from an academic point of view. One intriguing idea was the platform exploration phase was detached from the rest of the life cycle, sitting out in space spitting out great opportunities that would be realized as platforms as it went through the planning and development phases. People referred to that phase as *mythodology* as it was a pretty picture that nobody knew how to implement. For all three phases it was time to move to the next level of detail.

- With the major approval meetings, milestones, and synchronization points identified for each of the phases, exit criteria were developed that were a list of deliverables or work to be done at this point in the program. The exit criteria were grouped into buckets associated with all the organizations that contributed to work in that phase. The first release of the Platform Program Life Cycle was done by committee.

■ Work on the first corporate level Platform Program Life Cycle started at the end of 2004 and continued through all of 2005. By the time the PPLC was finally and officially released in February of 2006, it was a 77-page long masterpiece of cross-group discussion and input to achieve a pork barrel piece of PLC legislation. The now iconic PLC funnel, shown in Figure 8.2, never looked better.

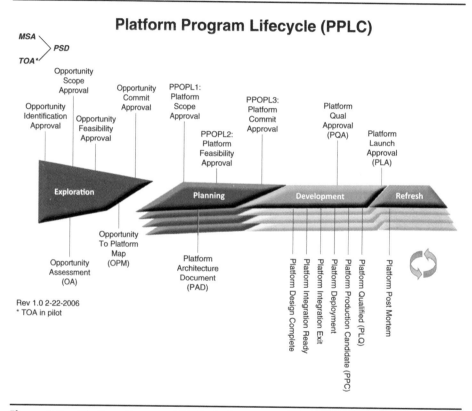

Figure 8.2 Platform Program Life Cycle *Source: Intel Platform Program and Product Life Cycle Specification – 2006*

The only problem was it didn't get used all that much. It was thick and some people called it a brick. As in the first releases of the PLC the first attempt at a platform life cycle was onerous.

Greg Welch – Mobile Strategic Planning 2006 *"From a planner's perspective the train ran off the track when it was micro-engineered. The team created a spec that no one could staff to execute. Not that it was wrong, we just couldn't do it."*

Going back to George Box's quote again "All models are wrong, but some models are useful." In this case the platform program life cycle PPLC 1.0 wasn't necessarily wrong; it just wasn't particularly useful.

In retrospect, PPLC Release 1.0 was really a conceptual prototype platform life cycle of new thinking. The job now was to take what was written down and make it real to the people doing the work. As before the job was to make the frame *work* for them, but as 2005 turned into 2006 there came a really big distraction.

Lessons Learned

■ Change at the corporate level will yield segments that "get there" sooner than other segments—plan for it.

■ Don't outstrip reality with broad, progressive change; start at the baseline and add strategically, taking the practitioners along with you.

■ Again, learn from your failures to redesign, rewrite, and improve the model.

Questions

1. What external environmental factors are driving internal models?

2. Are your product development models changing as fast as your business?

Chapter 9

Regain and Sustain

It is not necessary to change. Survival is not mandatory.

—W. Edward Deming

From the fourth quarter of 2005 through the second quarter of 2006, Intel microprocessors lost market share to AMD and the financial numbers were below expectations. The stated reasons were supply issues and inadequate microprocessor products. Intel had ridden the Pentium® 4 microarchitecture too long (5.5 years), giving AMD an opportunity to bring better products to market. It was time to double down on Intel's platform efforts and drive hard to bring the 65-nanometer dual-core microprocessor to market. There were two overarching strategies for 2006: One, regain and sustain technology leadership and two, add an equivalent focus on efficiency and costs.

Ready, SET, Go

If a company can have a midlife crisis, this was the time when the company began to wonder, am I getting middle-aged and way too fat and slow to respond? It was just like that middle-aged person who takes a long look in the mirror and that moment of realization is upon them…"Oh dear." In Intel's case the difference was that mirror was provided by an objective third party.

"During Q2 of 2006, in the face of poor technological and financial performance, Intel CEO Paul Otellini decided to create a Structure and Efficiency Team (SET). SET led by now-CFO Stacy Smith, would take 90 days to gather data for a top-to-bottom company review. SET aimed to reorganize Intel with lower cost structures, enabling Intel to compete in the lower-margin days ahead. According to Otellini, SET would make Intel a more nimble, agile company, able to quickly respond to customer demands and changing market conditions."

Structure and Efficiency Team – *Intelpedia*, modified 17 December 2007.

The objective third party was Bain Consulting. With Bain's help the SET team found that employees perceived decision making in the company as slow and poor. The sheer number of managers promoted bureaucracy and hindered decision making. The two-in-a-box managerial construct where two managers share a job had gotten out of control and was getting in the way of effective role clarity. Manager spans and levels were not optimized. There were organizations with more levels of management than needed and managers that had, in some cases, one to two direct reports.

By the summer of 2006, one thousand managerial positions were eliminated and the associated individuals terminated. With few exceptions the two-in-a-box construct was substantially reduced. Guidelines for spans and levels were rigorously enforced. During this time the average number of direct reports per manager went from 6 to 8.3. In addition to the number and levels of management, the focus was also on overhead in general.

Headcount and spending on IT, marketing, strategic planning, and human resources was higher than industry standards; in some cases it was much higher. Headcount was reduced in the above areas. Non-headcount spending was also reduced; programs were examined, consolidated or eliminated.

Nonprofitable businesses were sold or reestablished as a joint venture, which yielded more headcount reduction. In the second quarter of 2006, Intel employed 102,500 employees; by the end of the third quarter of 2007, the number was reduced to 88,000 and was still decreasing.

The SET team made customer orientation a focus topic. For too long Intel tried to dictate its products to customers. The focus was to make listening to our customers part of the company culture. Customer orientation became a bonus goal for 2007.

Responding to an outdated microarchitecture issue, the company committed itself to a tick-tock model where Intel would introduce a new manufacturing process every other year (the tick) or a new microarchitecture on the interleaving years (the tock). This model put Intel on a rigorous cadence targeted to put and keep the company one generation ahead in process technology and competitive in microarchitecture. This also served as a mechanism to manage risk by not changing too many things at once.

By the third quarter of 2007, it was clear the two objectives set in 2006 had been achieved. The 65-nanometer duo-core microprocessor had ramped in the marketplace. Market share was regained. Technological lead had been regained and the tick tock model would sustain that lead. The program to focus on efficiency and the headcount reductions contributed to profitability. By the third quarter of 2007, Intel was again delivering strong financial performance, but the focus on structure and efficiency did not abate.

It was during this 2007 timeframe that a look backward to the progress made against the platform transformation 2005 objectives was conducted. This was progress made during a time when regaining market share and SET were prominent in the mind of the company.

Platform Transformation Retrospective

Interviews were conducted across the breadth and depth of the company asking questions about progress and problems with platform transformation. Three open-ended questions were asked: what worked, what didn't work, and what does Intel need to do going forward? The aggregate answer to these questions made it seem that as a company we were confused.

Individuals were not confused, but their opinions were all over the map, thus as a company we were confused. If you were leading a platform organization you saw progress. The only difference person to person was how much progress. The first director of the Corporate Platform Office had moved on to lead the Server Group.

Diane Bryant – VP and Co-GM of the Server Group *"There has been a significant shift. No one questions that we are a platform company. Long gone are the days where the microprocessor development operated independent of the other platform components. Where we still need to evolve is in our end user focus —a focus on the user experience delivered by our platforms. We continue to work on a systematic way to drive the user experience into the PPLC.*

At the other end of the spectrum was manufacturing where many individuals in this organization didn't see any progress. Some thought that the big splash two years before that was just a bunch of marketing fluff. Somewhere in the middle were the ingredient people. They could understand the need from an intellectual level, but could see little benefit to their business. The "platform thing" didn't seem to improve their business, so the ingredient organizations were neutral on its importance.

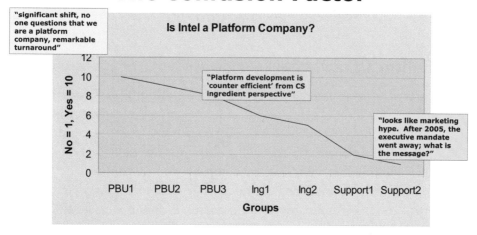

Figure: 9.1 The 2007 Confusion Factor Graph
Source: Platform Transformation Retrospective – 2007

Other factors added to the confusion, as illustrated in Figure 9.1. Many positions thought necessary to transform, like a strong platform program manager, did not happen as expected. Marketing believed customers didn't understand the platform idea so they rebranded the microprocessor. Many people who worked on usage models, which were important to the end user and therefore platform requirements, fell victim to the actions of SET. Were these actions part of the distractions on the competitive situation the year before?

Steve Smith – *"I think it (refocusing on core) was a huge distraction. At the time in 2005 when AMD crossed Intel in terms of performance and perception there was a renewed focus on 'the processor is it'; internally, competitively, and externally in the press. So, the second thing is our existing processer brands slipped in relevance. The press, the internal mindset of competitiveness, and the branding people all doubled down on the processor and I think, to my mind, quite confused the Intel audience that what was relevant was the processor and not the platform."*

As the results of the interviews were analyzed, an obvious question came through: Are we a microprocessor company or a platform company? At first the temptation was to choose one or the other. Intel doesn't sell platforms; it sells ingredients to companies that make platforms. The events of the recent past starkly defined the need to have best-in-class microprocessors. If you were playing poker, it would be like needing to have jacks or better to open. However, Intel also had to consider the needs of the end user and solutions that would be delivered at the platform level. This was essential for Intel to maintain relevance in the marketplace.

So to answer the question: Is Intel either a microprocessor company or a platform company? The strategic answer is both. Intel needed to design and deliver cutting edge microprocessors; this implies the latest and greatest technologies and manufacturing. But the long-term corporate health depends on having a platform strategy, which includes the end user experience. In addition to shipping best-in-class microprocessors, Intel needs to think, act, and execute like a platform company to maintain relevance in the marketplace. The second release of the Platform Program Life Cycle attempted to reflect this while focusing on regaining its own relevance in the product and platform development community.

Platform Program Life Cycle Revision 2.0

One reason the PPLC Revision 1.0 wasn't useful to the platform development community can be attributed to its "design by committee" feel. It contained lots of pork barrel life cycle legislation to add to benefit selfish interests of some members of the big committee. The second reason was the PPLC Revision 1.0 was really a prototype. It was the first experiment at a corporate level platform view of a life cycle. An old but true lesson: never productize the prototype. Revision 1.0 was a 71-page prototype available to be kicked around, tested, tried, and changed.

A much smaller team took the existing PPLC into the development community and simply asked what was wrong with it. It was much the same as the recovery from the first failed PLCs those many years before. Take something tangible into the community of people who develop products and work with them to make it useful to their needs. The goal was to make Revision 2.0 tight, crisp, and relevant. Focus improvements with the user in mind, in this case the development and planning teams.

Sarah Gregory *"If you ask people what they need you aren't going to get anything useful out of them, but if you say 'Go use this and tell me what's wrong with it,' you're better able to see what to do to make something that does work. When we did this we found the development community was able to describe the parts of the PPLC that didn't make sense and see what they were really trying to do and they'd tell us, 'Here is what was broken in the previous phase, because we weren't getting from them what we needed to be getting."*

Erik Simmons *"Well, that generally works because people are much more able to criticize something that exists than think of something that doesn't. I am not above creating something provocatively wrong if you can't get people to respond to a blank board. I'll come up with something wildly incorrect, throw it up there, they start criticizing it, and now we are getting somewhere."*

This was history repeating itself. The first two attempts at a PLC were defining prototypes of a PLC that were destined to be shot down and not relevant to the people doing the work, but as before they were attempts that were a starting point that could be useful if you listened to the people doing the work.

During the development of Revision 2.0, the reasons for each phase and the milestones within each phase were examined and reexamined for their usefulness. The ingredient PLC was updated and better integrated with the PPLC. The exit criteria for each milestone were simplified to the critical few and rationale was added to explain the reason for the exit criteria. The PPLC Revision 2.0 was not released as a printed, text-only specification, but as a web-based tool, in a web format, which supported just-in-time presentation of the milestone definitions and exit criteria. The web-based format satisfied numerous "ease of use" issues for the platform program manager. Instead of translating milestone exit criteria from a document to a working checklist, they could download the information in a format that supported quick tailoring. Figure 9.2 shows the home page for the web-based format.

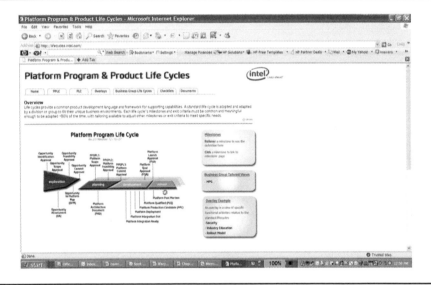

Figure 9.2   Source: Web-based Platform Program Lifecycle Revision 2.0 – circa 2008

Any Intel employee could move the cursor over any phase or milestone and an explanation would appear in the box at the left. The exit criteria for each milestone could be downloaded into an Excel† format to be used as a checklist, as shown in Figure 9.3. These decisions were made by an integration team consisting of members from across product development, empowered by their organizations to agree to and release a life cycle relevant to their organization.

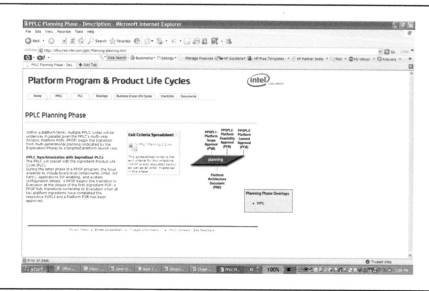

Figure 9.3   Phase Specific Details

The resulting PPLC Revision 2.0 released in 2007 proved useful to the program managers responsible for execution in the development phase of the PPLC. The server segment actually gave up their own group-specific version and started using the corporate PPLC Revision 2.0 as their life cycle model.

Bruce Wollstein – *"The direction servers went with the 'checklist' approach allowed the server PXT managers to decide which part of the corporate checklist applied to their platform. All groups had the same corporate starting point, but were tailored to meet the platform needs."*

The planning phase more closely resembled reality. The combination of usage/technology/business was built into the exit criteria. Some of the more advanced planning teams were successful in getting the platform planning ahead of the microprocessor planning as was the original intent of platform transformation. Consider the lead-in to an article shown below from the server planning organization.

"Among the many challenges involved in meeting this objective, perhaps the most critical was getting platform planning ahead of ingredient (e.g. CPU) planning so the platform would define the components versus our status quo process of long lead-time components locking down well ahead of platform definitions.

Since no one knew exactly how to begin to make this transformation happen, the Server Platform Architecture and Planning (SPAP) team dove headfirst into the challenge and spent the better part of last year working on it. The team successfully demonstrated how to move forward on transforming Intel to a platform company, and not only demonstrated how to get the platform ahead of component planning, but the new process also generated higher-quality product definitions and more efficient planning."

– Stepping up to the Platform Transformation Challenge, Kerry Miller and Chris Galluzzo, September 2007

While the PPLC Revision 2.0 provided improved usage for planners and execution program managers, it missed one key use case, the business manager who depended on the life cycle to set expectations.

As 2007 turned into 2008, the PPLC Revision 2.0 and its associated PLCs were deployed and used. Given the length of the development cycles it took a while to see what was useful and what was not. The year 2008 started out as a banner year, but then came the fourth quarter of that year and what would be known as the Great Recession. As Intel became one of those companies that led the recovery, it became clear on the other side business had changed and among those many things within Intel that would have to change in response would be its platform and product life cycles.

Lessons Learned

- Companies and organizations can become out-of-shape and over-weight, the equivalent of a midlife crisis in people. When this happens, serious structural change is required to "trim down" and "shape up."

- Management structure can have significant affect on decision-making effectiveness.

- As with products, life cycle models must be "used" by the development community or they are irrelevant.

Questions

1. Does your organization have indicators in place to alert you before the organization becomes overweight and out of shape?

2. Does your life cycle support gathering the information needed to give a heads up on viability?

3. Are decisions made once at the appropriate management level and do they stick?

4. Is the continuous improvement element of your life cycle visible and usable by the practitioners?

Chapter 10

PLC Next

Most of the important things in the world have been accomplished by people who have kept trying when there seemed to be no hope at all.

—Dale Carnegie

As 2009 became 2010, Intel was among the companies leading the way out of the Great Recession, but the world Intel now competed in was different. Between these two years there came *Avatar,* the iPad[†] personal "apps," and by July of 2010 over 500 million active Facebook[†] users. There was now a new primacy of the end user, a global shift in geographies and demographics, a shift to cloud computing, and the defining ultra-mobile device. Intel needed to adapt and so did its life cycles.

It had been three years since the last major release of the platform and ingredient life cycles. This was a long span of time between major releases. Businesses needed a life cycle more relevant to their changing competitive needs. The traditional businesses needed to have a more predictable and metronomic life cycle while the new businesses needed greater flexibility and adaptability. Both needed to be more connected to the experience the end user would have that would contain or be Intel products. A comprehension of the complete solution was needed. It was time to take a step back and study deeply the product development environment the PLC supported.

As always, the life cycles needed to be the memory system of what the organization knows works while pushing the envelope on the next phase of maturity and relevance over a defined period of time. The only difference was that the environment was changing faster than anticipated in many areas.

The PLC Environmental Assessment

Critical to defining the next release or the next series of releases of the PLC at Intel was to understand the environment the PLC served. Over an extended time, what will be going on in the world? What will that mean for product and service opportunities for Intel? How will all of that define the requirements of a life cycle or set of life cycles at Intel?

Representatives of different businesses and job functions gathered for the workshop to complete the assessment. In brainstorming about the future, summarized information from environmental assessments in the businesses was reviewed in addition to the history of the life cycles to date. Future trends were identified along with assumptions, both explicit and implicit, regarding the environment the PLC supported. Assumptions are deeply held beliefs that often constrain thinking and were therefore documented and challenged. Future trends have implications that must be logically connected to the strategic requirements of the next PLC and answered in future modifications. Examples of trends and their implications are as follows:

Divergent needs will grow. The emergence of System on a Chip (SoC) is redefining traditional silicon development. This means a separation of the creation of intellectual property (IP) both inside and outside the company and the integration of this IP into specific product instances and their derivatives. Software's growing importance and prevalence will put different demands on the PLC as the current phases and milestones do not reflect the blurred lines between silicon, software, and hardware activities. Technology development remains different from product development, but they need to be better synchronized than they have been.

The implications of this trend include the following:

■ PLC stages and metrics need to capture both technology and product attributes and measures as well as metrics.

■ The traditional linear flow of the PLC may need to be adapted to agile development where planning and development occur simultaneously. The current overlap model does not adequately capture this concurrent activity.

■ Technology and product development need to be able to be separated and the PLC needs to acknowledge that not every technology project will have the same types of metrics at various stages.

■ The PLC may need to adapt to a product tree approach rather than a single, project-by-project approach.

■ PLC terms may need to be adapted or morphed to accommodate the realities of SoC and solutions development.

■ Open innovation is not adequately supported by the PLC. Modifications need to reflect technology coming from outside Intel.

Convergent needs will grow. The focus on solutions will take the work started during Intel's platform transformation and drive it to a new level. Cross-organization complexity will increase. Multiple teams will be involved in development. The PLC is used for integration across teams. The PLC will need to be valuable to teams from different corporate cultures as a "translator" between development activities, and the need will increase as acquisitions increase. Consistent definitions are needed across the life cycle, but flexibility in adopting the life cycle to specific project types is also needed.

Implications of this trend include the following:

■ While common definitions within the PLC are needed to support cross-team interaction, the PLC needs to be flexible enough to be adapted to the various types of products as well as the various cultures of development teams. This need will increase with acquisitions.

■ The PLC needs to continue to be expressed as a framework and play an integration role and a communication tool across teams.

■ The PLC needs to be updated on a regular basis to adequately capture the changing nature of development and the multiple cultures using the tool.

■ Systems engineering approaches will need to be incorporated into the PLC and combined with end-to-end requirements engineering.

User experience will grow as a focus area. A solutions focus is becoming more prevalent across Intel. Solutions development doesn't work the same way as technology and product development projects. Metrics and capabilities are needed to better reflect the user experience across the PLC.

Implications of this trend include the following:

■ User experience needs to be defined in the context of each stage and in a traceable way across stages.

■ Metrics for the user experience need to be developed and incorporated into the PLC.

The need for the business case will grow. Current metrics are too focused on product attributes. Future uses of the PLC may need more business related metrics to be useful across teams and at various decision making levels.

From these trends and implications, strategic deltas were identified, which in turn led to the identification of strategic vectors meant to guide the evolution of the PLC for the next several releases.

PLC Strategic Vectors

The basic framework of the PLC remains a north star to product development. It guides if appropriately used. It is a framework and a synchronization tool, but going forward the PLC needs to evolve strategically in the following areas:

Connect a corporate high level framework. How do you balance the needs of convergence and divergence? On one hand you have the specialized needs of very different business units. The needs of software versus SoC are examples. One the other hand you have businesses, including different market segments, subsidiaries, and different companies that need to work together to develop compelling solutions. How do you accomplish the needs of the divergent and convergent forces?

Jonathon Walsh, Intel Architecture Software Program Director – *"The focus on solutions coming from the development of many organizations demands that you break through the silo'd organizations if only to have a sensible conversation to orient the work and make decisions. At a certain level you must have a consistent definition and application of terms, quality criteria, practices, and measurements throughout the product life cycle. At the same time there must be the flexibility to adapt the common corporate framework to specialized development such as software. Your PLC must do both."*

The answer is a layered framework. There needs to be a framework that is common enough for the various interests to communicate with each other. From a general manager's point of view this needs to be more detailed than when you start a project and ready it for launch. It needs to be that set of synchronization points that any competent business person would relate to such as, when do you make your investing commitment, when do you think you have designed something worthy of evaluation, when do you think the design has been vetted sufficiently, and when do you think it is ready for launch into the marketplace.

If the different businesses can agree to the top level, then click down one more level to the business-specific specialized need. Note that the program manager's needs are not orthogonal to the common framework.

For example:

- If software needs to map their development effort to a long lead time ingredient, like a microprocessor, then appreciate that not all software can be defined and developed at the same time. Some basic software can be defined and developed along with the microprocessor, but other software will need to be defined and developed in later stages of the microprocessor or its associated platform development.

- If SoC differs from traditional silicon development at Intel in terms of both cadences, reuse, and deploying derivative products, then express this under the common framework.

- If technology development is different than product development, then accept that, but take the time to better synchronize the technology development activity with the product development activities.

Create user experience–driven product development. What are the objectives of the end user experience even if you as a company don't control the user experience? The objective would be to first map the user-driven experience across the life cycle. Going from left to right along the life cycle ties ethnographic research in the exploration phase to user experience objectives to usage models and use case development, which in turn translates to platform and ingredient requirements that can be verified, validated, and qualified prior to launch.

With the mapping completed, gaps in this seamless map could be identified including those outside the company that control this experience. A roadmap to close the gaps would then be laid out over a multiyear period. The gaps exist along the PLC and across the different business units.

This would also mean that the user experience and usage models would emerge as a driver in technology selection. High priority use cases would be identified based on experience, and technology selection would in part be based on which technologies would be best suited to satisfy the high priority use cases.

Justin Rattner – *"Intel's planning process needs to move away from the tradition of focusing on individual features and fundamentally incorporate user experience design into the process"*

Sarah Gregory – *"Usage was marginalized for so long we gave it the equivalent of Affirmation Action to draw extra attention to it. Going forward usage must remain important, but it must be in balance with the needs of technology development and the business case. Entry into the PLC could come from any of these vectors, but there must be balance between the three."*

Follow the money, Part II. Improve the utilization of the framework to connect platform and product development portfolios to Intel's corporate strategic planning calendar by aligning market, technology, and product strategy to product planning and delivery. To escape the exploration phase mythodology, define a practical way to navigate the connection between corporate strategic planning, organization platform and ingredient planning, and the development action to realize the results.

This would include:

- A detailed analysis of the environment to include trends and assumptions. Trends and the triggers that let you know they are actually happening as forecasted.

- Assumptions, both explicate and implicate, are documented as they are deeply held beliefs that could constrain thinking.

- Definition of long-term business goals and scenarios for accomplishing these goals. These become the business strategies.

- A multiyear plan that makes these plans operational, connects strategy to action, and provides a launch pad into the planning phase for specific ingredient and platform instances.

Russ Martinelli – *"Strategies are just words in documents if not followed by aligned execution via the PLC. The PLC is the intercept between strategy and execution. Investments are defined in exploration and planning are all about figuring out how you execute your strategy. The PLC provides the framework to connect your execution to your strategy."*

Anticipate and embrace SoC. The new and different life cycle for SoC development with its IP block development reuse, fast cadence, and use of derivatives, is a departure from traditional Intel silicon development, but through the lessons achieved in SoC, it has influenced and will continue to influence traditional silicon product development.

Paul Ryan – *" SoC is a fundamentally different vision of synchronized maturity. Get the intellectual property (IP) mature much earlier than you have in the past so you can make decisions about product much later than you have in the past."*

Leverage systems engineering. With the increased focus on vertically oriented businesses, the PLC framework needs to proactively respond by applying systems engineering to the life cycle.

Erik Simmons - *"Systems engineering is a multidisciplinary approach to transforming needs, requirements and constraints into a successful system. Systems engineering principles and practices help ensure a focus on the overall end product, not just on components or interim results. Continuously increasing system scope and complexity makes systems engineering an important skill to optimize final results, and often to get results at all. We need to see how to apply the principles of systems engineering on the problems we face."*

A traditional model would be to follow the traditional systems engineer "V", the wants, needs, and desires of the end user need to be identified and subsequently decomposed to the system, subsystem, and ingredient elements to be recomposed going up the other side to ensure it is validated at the ingredient, subsystem, and system level against those want needs and desires of the end user.

These are the strategic vectors for the next PLC. They are new but as the environment so different that the lessons learned from the first fifteen years are not relevant for the PLC going forward. Let us examine those key lessons and gauge their applicability going forward.

Back to the Future

Even as the strategic vectors for the future will take the PLC to places it has never been before, some things will not change. These are the timeless truisms learned over the years. Upon reflection, these truisms from life cycle history are really what makes the life cycle "frame" work:

1. *Make the PLC relevant.* Does it solve a business problem for the people getting the work done? Is the cost of implementing and following the PLC greater than any possible value? If it doesn't solve a business problem or costs more than its benefits, it will be ignored.

2. *The PLC alone is not enough.* The PLC is a framework from which you can hang other processes and capabilities. The PLC, in concert with other processes and capabilities, yields business results. A PLC that is connected to the decision making structure that makes product and investment decisions will be more relevant to the organization and thus more successful.

3. *Platform thinking.* The need to manage complexity drives the need for platform thinking and it is that thinking that begins to focus on the solutions important to the end user.

Future revisions of the PLC can add value in multiple ways. First, the framework can anticipate organizational, competitive, and technical trouble areas. One example of an opportunity is to address the need for usage information across the life cycle. The life cycle and capability owners can work together to continuously research best practices and translate them into practical use in partnership with the product development businesses. About every two years the life cycle can be refreshed to reflect what the businesses have learned during application of the current revision.

Vivek Tiwari – Director Corporate Platform Office 2011 *"The one constant in the semiconductor industry over the last few decades has been the rate of change – as enshrined in Moore's Law. The PLC thus needs to evolve as well. For the next phase in this evolution the things that we need to focus on are the integration of hardware and software and a holistic approach to security and user-experience. We are at an exciting phase in the evolution of the industry and the PLC is at the heart of it"*

As this book goes to publication Intel is experiencing rapidly evolving times. Some call it an inflection point. There will be case studies written about these times in the future regardless of the outcome. May the outcome be positive for Intel and may the business unit adoption of the PLC have helped in some small way.

Afterword

Life is full of delicious irony. We were sitting in a booth at a local Hillsboro restaurant talking across the table with Stuart Douglas, a program manager with Intel Press. Stuart is a Scotsman who has been in the states for awhile. Such a long time that you would think he would lose his accent, but delightfully he had not. He kept calling our book a "booook." We had talked with him about a year and a half before and now we had called him the week before telling him we had half the chapters done. This prompted several actions including this luncheon meeting.

The scene: Stuart is sitting across the table from Chris and Deanna; he is smiling, but with a serious and purposeful demeanor.

The dialog goes like this:

Stuart: "I think I mentioned the last time we talked that we have taken your PLC and adopted it at Intel Press." Chris and Deanna have a vague recollection of this, but we aren't clear on why we should care at this point.

Stuart: "All the books that go through Intel Press follow it. That means your project needs to follow it." Our vague recollection turns to shock and total silence. But Stuart is not deterred; he's seen the look before and pushes on.

Stuart: "You will have to resubmit you project proposal and get the review committee to accept it as an Intel Press project." We are still thinking that this sounds pretty much like the initial product opportunity proposal

(PLC POP). Okay, we know what that is; we can do that. Our heads start to nod; smiles return.

Stuart: "Then we need a detailed outline…for your project I think twenty pages would do."

Chris and Deanna: "Okay, sure, we can do that." We are thinking that would be the moral equivalent of a landing zone.

Stuart: "When the editor is halfway through the content we will launch a 'go-to-market' plan." Chris and Deanna are thinking: You have got to be kidding!

Stuart: "This includes cover design, who is going to do your foreword, and your validation plan."

Chris: "A validation plan?"

Stuart: "With roughly twenty-five people who we can use to test the acceptance of you material."

Chris: "So basically testing its fitness for use defined before we get approval?"

Stuart: "Yes, precisely."

Chris: "But we are already halfway done with the book…."

Stuart: "Then I would think the outlining part of the process will not be difficult."

So there it was. We were just like those engineers that dive right into development without the reasonable and proper upfront planning and preparation. Here was an organization that took the PLC we helped drive across the company, had adapted it to their business, and now used it on us!

So with a gun to our head we filled out the proposal template and submitted it to committee and it was accepted. And then we filled out the outline template and put in enough detail to get it past the twenty-page target and it was accepted. The go-to-market activities were ticked off one after another leading up to the long-anticipated milestone borrowed from some PLC called First Customer Ship. In retrospect the process was rigorous and kept us organized; if we did another project with Intel Press we would start off with their version of a PLC or some future improved version of a PLC, but it stops and makes you wonder…Is it possible you couldn't actually live in a world you are trying to help create?

Appendix A

Life Cycles Overview

Life cycles provide a high-level framework by which an organization can manage the development of products from inception through end of life. Life cycles can also document a common product development language and provide structure for supporting capabilities.

A standard corporate life cycle is adopted and adapted by divisions or sub-groups to fit their unique business environments. Each new release of the corporate life cycle is a reflection of the company's evolving thinking around product and platform development. Life cycle milestones and exit criteria at the corporate level must be common and meaningful enough to be adopted about 80 percent of the time, allowing for about 20 percent tailoring by the businesses to meet specific needs.

Life cycles and their supporting capabilities can affect product development in these areas:

- Increased development efficiency
- Accelerated time to money by minimizing risk and reducing rework
- Synchronized and stable roadmaps
- Clear decision making
- Common language and goals where organizations interact with each other and customers; example: marketing and sampling

How Common Do We Need to Be?

What is the business value in using and maintaining a common framework and language? There is business value where organizations are:

- Selling to common customers across different business groups. Where customer sample expectations are the same for all products produced by your company.

- Sharing ingredients to define multiple platforms. Effective alignment of a product life cycle to multiple platform life cycles includes shared levels of quality and customer expectations.

- Developing products against the same or similar customer expectations on cadence.

Why a Corporate Life Cycle Framework?

The corporate-wide framework provides a "structure" or "a skeleton" on which multiple business groups and functional groups can build or "overlay" their work and show how what they do relates to product development. Some of these "overlays" show the relationship of supporting methods, practices, and processes to the framework.

With the framework we can demonstrate the alignment of product development to other global processes and foster a common language.

Figure A.1, a graphic from the late 1990s, shows how multiple disciplines can map their unique milestones to the higher level framework.

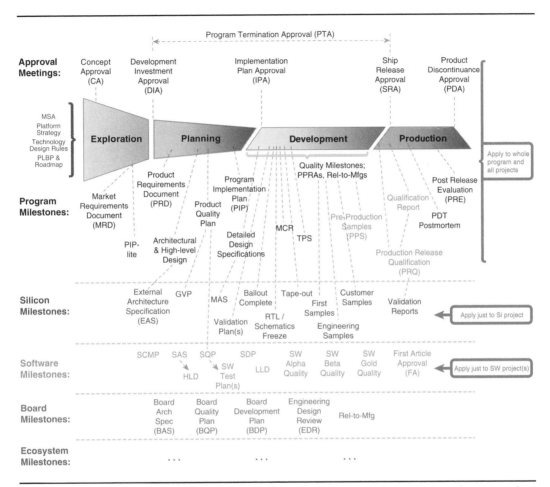

Figure A.1   Multiple Disciplines Map Their Unique Milestones to the Higher Level Framework

What Are the Benefits of a Life Cycle at the Team Level?

When defined correctly, a life cycle provides a common product development language and framework for supporting capabilities; that is, requirements engineering, retrospectives, program management, feedback mechanisms, scheduling, risk management, and so on.

A team's success using a life cycle is measured by predictability across all the vectors of the program:

■ Common product development language

■ Feasible and realistic planning

■ Improved communication between platform/ingredient teams across organizational boundaries

■ Informed decision making with regards to delivery/features/quality

■ Efficient project execution

■ Visibility into project status versus plan

■ Control and reliable delivery of quality at release milestones

■ Phased commitment of resources

The framework provides the structure for continuous improvement, innovation, and standards at the appropriate level.

How Is Success Measured?

Success is measured by predictability across all program vectors (schedule, resource, risk, and so on).

Program-to-program improvement is achieved by gleaning new and innovative methods, best-known methods (BKMs), and feeding them to the next program and back into the framework or supporting capability.

The life cycle is a reflection of the company's evolving thinking about product development.

The goals of the framework are to define a common intent, with enough flexibility to meet unique business goals. In addition, a common life cycle supports the product development teams in meeting its commitments and in continuous improvement.

The life cycle framework provides a location on which we can hang multiple product development processes, methods, and capabilities:

■ Opportunity definition and assessment

■ Product planning

■ Usage definition and requirements engineering

■ Program management

■ Product integration and validation

■ Risk and schedule management

Life Cycle Phases

Most life cycles have four or five phases: Exploration, Planning, Development, Production and the "Fifth" Phase, which can have a variety of names as you'll see below.

Exploration Phase

Sometimes called the "fuzzy front-end," the exploration phase incorporates business inputs from market analysis, business strategy and imperatives, platform and product-line planning, and technology initiatives along with customer feedback. The work done consists of an analysis of the business case for the product, available resources, and divisional capabilities to pursue product development. A designated cross-functional team comprised of marketing, engineering, and finance evaluate a product opportunity and determine whether to commit the division to developing the product. This phase concludes with the approval for development investment expenditures (funding and resources) to take the product into the planning phase.

Planning Phase

During the planning phase, a cross-functional team defines the scope, feasibility, and plan of record (POR) for the product. This definition is documented in the form of product requirements, design documents, and quality plans, to enable all functional areas to perform the due-diligent planning used to establish the program POR. The program POR defines the organization's commitments regarding product features to be delivered at various releases, delivery dates for interim and final product releases, product quality levels, product and program cost, and pre-ship release approvals for design wins.

Development Phase

Often called "execution," in the development phase, the product is engineered, developed, and evaluated against its requirements and program criteria. This phase may involve multiple pre-production releases.

Production

Launch or make and ship! During the production phase, manufacturing, sales, and service activities are ramped up to support full product availability across all targeted segments and geographies. During this phase, key lessons are defined and driven into in-flight and future development efforts.

The Fifth Phase

Possible names are Maintenance, End-of-Life, and Post-Production. Support services are still active for the product until full implementation of the Support End of Life Plan occurs. At the appropriate time, product discontinuance is planned and carried out.

Milestones and Exit Criteria

Milestones are checkpoints or synchronization points, not gates. The work does not "stop" and wait for a decision from management; work continues towards the documented expectations. Exit criteria for a milestone helps describe the state of what has been produced to this point and expectations for quality level. At the life cycle framework level, we do not define how to produce the deliverable.

Overlays

Overlays are a representation of a business group or functional area's work against the common framework. They provide a way for functional and/or organizational intersections with product development. Overlays allow the graphic display of the myriad of activities required to produce even the simplest product. Examples of functional overlays are security, customer support and service, field sales, regulations, ecology and environmental standards.

Internal business partners see opportunity in connecting their work to the life cycles and relating what they provide to product development. For this reason, the life cycles must be flexible enough to be used across the corporation in multiple product types and functions.

Index

Continuing Education is Essential

It's a challenge we all face – keeping pace with constant change in information technology. Whether our formal training was recent or long ago, we must all find time to keep ourselves educated and up to date in spite of the daily time pressures of our profession.

Intel produces technical books to help the industry learn about the latest technologies. The focus of these publications spans the basic motivation and origin for a technology through its practical application.

Right books, right time, from the experts

These technical books are planned to synchronize with roadmaps for technology and platforms, in order to give the industry a head-start. They provide new insights, in an engineer-to-engineer voice, from named experts. Sharing proven insights and design methods is intended to make it more practical for you to embrace the latest technology with greater design freedom and reduced risks.

I encourage you to take full advantage of Intel Press books as a way to dive deeper into the latest technologies, as you plan and develop your next generation products. They are an essential tool for every practicing engineer or programmer. I hope you will make them a part of your continuing education tool box.

Sincerely,

Senior Fellow and Chief Technology Officer Intel Corporation

Turn the page to learn about titles from Intel Press for system developers

Managing Information Technology for Business Value

Practical Strategies for IT and Business Managers
By Martin Curley
ISBN 0-9717861-7-8

Managing Information Technology for Business Value is Martin Curley's call for IT and business managers to reformulate the way they manage IT. Traditionally, IT success has been measured in terms of IT parameters such as up time, capacity, and processing speed.

It is Curley's contention that if IT is to deliver business value, IT should be measured in core business terms---for example, customer satisfaction, revenue growth, and profitability.

At a time when some corporations are reducing IT spending and once again looking at IT as a cost center, Martin Curley's Managing Information Technology for Business Value provides a necessary and timely counterbalance.

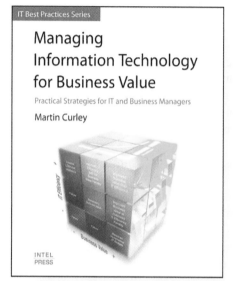

IT Best Practices Series

Managing
Information Technology
for Business Value

Practical Strategies for IT and Business Managers

Martin Curley

INTEL
PRESS

"Curley's book is required reading for all IT e:
-- *Professor Paul Tallon,*
Carroll School of Management, Boston College

"Curley shines a light on the path ahead for ambitious users of IT. If you have any impact on how IT gets used in your organization, you owe it to your shareholders to read this book. It will impact your bottom line!"
-- *John Fleming, CEO, Enzo Consulting*

"Martin Curley is a valued member of two very different communities---one populated by theorists who invent better methods to manage enterprises and the other populated by practitioners who put these methods to use."
-- *Jeanne Ross, Principal Research Scientist, MIT Sloan Center for Information Systems Research*

Measuring the Business Value of Information Technology

Practical Strategies for IT and Business Managers

By David Sward

ISBN 0-9764832-7-0

In today's fast moving competitive business environment, companies increasingly demand that IT investments demonstrate business value through measurable results. Intended for IT professionals and consultants as well as business managers, this book covers one of the most important strategies any company can establish to help manage IT in the coming years. Namely, the creation of an IT Business Value customer focused approaches to determine the business value for any IT investment an organization may make. Based on financial concepts and drawing on his background as a Human Factors Engineer, Sward makes the case that the process of establishing and running a business value program can ultimately create a new mindset for IT professionals. While Sward

recognizes this will not happen overnight, he believes it serves to instill a belief that an organization can and will create a competitive advantage and increase shareholder value not by just deploying information technology, but by deploying the *right* information technology by linking IT to corporate objectives and focusing all efforts on the requirements of the end user.

"David Sward explains the why's, what's, and how's of IT value measurement, presents an intuitively appealing vocabulary, and offers an impressive portfolio of instruments to manage IT investments to produce measured business value."

—*Lars Mathiassen, Professor, Computer Information Systems, Georgia State University*

"Intel's IT Business Value program deserves to be widely emulated. David Sward was one of the program's founders, and he gives the inside details on how it was developed and implemented. This book should influence IT investment and management practices for years to come."

—*Robert Laubacher, Research Associate, MIT Sloan School of Management*

Managing IT Innovation for Business Value

Practical Strategies for IT and Business Managers

By Esther Baldwin and Martin Curley

ISBN 1-934053-04-X

Successful companies actively cultivate new ideas, put those ideas to work quickly and efficiently, and harvest the business value benefits of successful innovations. Discussions of innovation often focus on what a company offers, that is, its products and services. In *Managing Information Technology Innovation for Business Value*, Esther Baldwin and Martin Curley show how successful IT innovations pay back handsomely as well. Innovation is not just about what a company offers, innovation is also about how a company conducts business and how IT innovation can transform an organization into a significantly more efficient company.

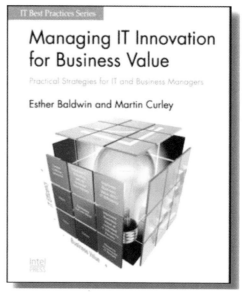

Drawing on their experience with innovation in Intel's engineering operations, Baldwin and Curley emphasize that IT innovation does not require whole-scale invention. An innovative IT solution reapplied in a new context can provide even greater business value because the initial investment in developing the solution has already been made.

Managing Information Technology Innovation for Business Value includes examples and case studies from IT organizations as well as from Intel Corporation. It also includes assessment techniques, skill set descriptions, and a capability maturity framework to help IT organizations understand where they stand as innovators and what steps they can take to strengthen their competencies.

"Innovation is not just about new products and services. It's also about how an innovative organization conducts business practices and the invaluable role of IT in those processes. For innovation to 'stick' it must become a systemic mindset like quality and safety. *Managing Information Technology Innovation for Business Value* offers invaluable and fresh stories that can be applied to any size IT organization."
— *Charles Chic Thompson, Batten Fellow at the UVA Darden Business School*

"What can a small-medium business (SMB) learn from the IT experts at Intel? Some common-sense lessons on IT innovation management. Innovation can be incremental, for example, and a proven innovation can be re-applied over and over in new and different settings. That's a key message for those of us who serve the SMB market"
— *Mathew Dickerson, AXXIS Technology, Australia.*

Special Deals, Special Prices!

To ensure you have all the latest books
and enjoy aggressively priced discounts,
please go to this Web site:

www.intel.com/intelpress/bookbundles.htm

Bundles of our books are available,
selected especially to address the needs
of the developer. The bundles place
important complementary topics at
your fingertips, and the price for a
bundle is substantially less than
buying all the books individually.

About Intel Press

Intel Press is the authoritative source of timely, technical books to help software and hardware developers speed up their development process. We collaborate only with leading industry experts to deliver reliable, first-to-market information about the latest technologies, processes, and strategies.

Our products are planned with the help of many people in the developer community and we encourage you to consider becoming a customer advisor. If you would like to help us and gain additional advance insight to the latest technologies, we encourage you to consider the Intel Press Customer Advisor Program. You can **register** here:

www.intel.com/intelpress/register.htm

For information about bulk orders or corporate sales, please send email to
bulkbooksales@intel.com

Other Developer Resources from Intel

At these Web sites you can also find valuable technical information and resources for developers:

www.intel.com/technology/rr	Recommended Reading list for books of interest to developers
www.intel.com/technology/itj	Intel Technology Journal
developer.intel.com	General information for developers
www.intel.com/software	Content, tools, training, and the Intel Early Access Program for software developers
www.intel.com/software/products	Programming tools to help you develop high-performance applications
www.intel.com/embedded	Solutions and resources for embedded and communications

If serial number is missing, please send an
e-mail to Intel Press at intelpress@intel.com

6185-0187-0584-6640

IMPORTANT

You can access the companion Web site for this book on
the Internet at:

www.intel.com/intelpress/plc

Use the serial number located in the upper-right hand
corner of this page to register your book and access
additional material, including the Digital Edition of
the book.